Researches

on

Meteorites

Researches

on

Meteorites

Edited by

CARLETON B. MOORE

Assistant Professor of Chemistry and Geology
Director, Nininger Meteorite Collection
Arizona State University

JOHN WILEY & SONS, INC., NEW YORK and LONDON

Contributors

JAMES R. ARNOLD, Professor of Chemistry, University of California, San Diego, LaJolla, California

PARAMATMA S. GOEL, Department of Chemistry, Carnegie Institute of Technology, Pittsburgh, Pennsylvania and Tata Institute of Fundamental Research, Bombay, India

MASATAKE HONDA, School of Science and Engineering, University of California, LaJolla, California.

TRUMAN P. KOHMAN, Professor of Chemistry, Carnegie Institute of Technology, Pittsburgh, Pennsylvania

E.L.KRINOV, Scientific Secretary of the Committee on Meteorites of the U.S.S.R. Academy of Sciences, Moscow, U.S.S.R.

DEVENDRA LAL, Tata Institute for Fundamental Research, Bombay, India

JOHN F. LOVERING, Department of Geophysics, Australian National University, Canberra, A.C.T. Australia

G.K.MANNING, Technical Manager, Metallurgy Department Battelle Memorial Institute, Columbus, Ohio

ROBERT E. MARINGER, Assistant Chief, Metals Science Group, Battelle Memorial Institute, Columbus, Ohio

BRIAN MASON, Curator of Mineralogy, The American Museum of Natural History, New York, New York

T.B.Masselski, Mellon Institute, Pittsburgh, Pennsylvania

CARLETON B. MOORE, Assistant Professor of Chemistry and Geology, Director of the Nininger Meteorite Collection, Arizona State University, Tempe, Arizona

ALFRED O.C.NIER, Chairman, School of Physics, University of Minnesota, Minneapolis, Minnesota

H.H.NININGER, Sedona, Arizona

A.E.RINGWOOD, Department of Geophysics, Australian National University, Canberra, A.C.T. Australia

PETER SIGNER, School of Physics, University of Minnesota, Minneapolis, Minnesota

Preface

The great immediate interest in the problems related to interplanetary space has resulted in a strong and essential interest on the investigation of meteorites. These bodies are the only major source of extra-terrestrial matter we have available for study.

The investigation and determination of the properties of meteoritic material requires the concerted efforts of investigators in all of the physical sciences: chemistry, physics, astronomy, astrophysics, and many of the special fields in the earth sciences. It is only through a joint effort that we can begin to unravel the problems in meteorites.

The characteristic pattern of present-day research is one of intensive individual efforts, only partially correlated, as investigators pursue their individual interests. The result of such a method of attack is that much of their findings are distributed in diverse scientific journals and less widely distributed organs of information distribution. This complicates the efforts of both professionals and those in training in keeping up-to-date on all the ramifications of this important area of scientific inquiry.

In order to help coordinate the efforts of the
investigators in the many fields related to meteoritics, Arizona State University held a meteorite symposium on March 10, 1961. The symposium was part of the program honoring the in-
auguration of Dr. G. Homer Durham as President
of Arizona State University. It also announced
the transfer of the outstanding Nininger Meteorite Collection to Arizona State University.
Through the efforts of Dr. H. H. Nininger, Mr.
George Boyd, Coordinator of Research at Arizona
State University and Mr. Herbert Fales of the
International Nickel Company, and with financial
aid from the Arizona State University Foundation
and the National Science Foundation, the Nininger
Meteorite Collection was established primarily
for purposes of scientific research by qualified
scientists throughout the nation.

The theme of the symposium was a review and
discussion of the current problems in meteoritics
and those which will probably be answered by
future research on meteorties. An attempt was
made to have the problems and contributions from
all the disciplines related to meteoritics represented. Both those contributions transmitted
orally at the symposium and those given by title
have been assembled in this volume, Researches
on Meteorites.

The contributions included represent a reasonable although certainly not complete cross section of current research interests. New developments in the study of iron meteorites are presented by Massalski (metallurgy) and Maringer
and Manning (deformation and thermal alterations).
Nuclear studies are covered by Signer and Nier
(rare gases in irons), Goel and Kohman (C^{14}) Goel
(production rates) and Arnold, Honda and Lal
(cosmic ray history). Some of the mineralogical
and petrological aspects are reviewed by Mason
(minerals of meteorites) and Moore (achondrites).
The relationship of meteorite studies to the
Earth is treated by Ringwood (chondritic earth
model) and Lovering (evolution of the meteorites)
is concerned with their origin. Krinov (meteor-

itics) and Nininger (meteorite recovery) discuss
the importance of meteorite investigations and
problems of specimen recovery and use. Papers
presented by Harrison Brown (statistics of meteorite falls) and Gerard Kuiper (collisions
among the asteroids) at the symposium have unfortunately not been included in these proceedings.

The essays generally review the current status
of research in each area, describe the author's
recent work and contain a pertinent bibliography.

Limitations on time prevented contributions
from other areas of interest from being included.
Although this volume does not include all the
fields of immediate interest, I hope that it
will prove useful in enlightening workers of the
activity in fields related to their own, and
provide investigators not actively engaged in
meteorite work with an outline of problems of
current interest.

I am indebted to many colleagues for advice in
the choice of contributors. The cooperation of
Dr. George Bateman, Mr. George Boyd and Mr. Ben
Jones of Arizona State University in matters
related to the arrangements for the symposium
are especially appreciated. The help of Mrs.
Lilian L. Shiman and Mrs. Jeanne S. Rich in pre-
paring the final copy was invaluable.

                                Carleton B. Moore

Arizona State University
Tempe, Arizona
September 10, 1961

Contents

E. L. KRINOV

U.S.S.R. Academy of Sciences

The Subject and Contents of Meteoritics as a Special Domain of Science

By the turn of the century, the study of meteorites had synthesized into an independent
domain of science. Its inception, however, dated back a hundred years (Krinov, 1960, 1949) to
the publication in 1794 of "Uber den Ursprung
der von Pallas gefundenen und anderer ihr ahnlicher Eisenmassen" by E.F.F.Chladni, (1794) a
researcher at the University of Berlin. The
book was published in German in Riga, Russia.
Here Chladni first presented scientific proof
of the actual fall of meteorites on the Earth
and authentic reports of eyewitnesses in various
countries. Chladni's inferences were founded
mainly on his study of the famous Pallas Iron -
meteorite. The latter, an iron-stony meteorite
with an original weight of 687 kg, was adopted
as typical of the class of meteorites known as
pallasites. Pallas Iron was found in 1749 on
the banks of the Yenissei River in Siberia by a
blacksmith named Medvedyev who thought it contained "something better than iron". The people
here told Medvedyev that the iron boulder he
found had fallen from the sky.
 In 1772 Medvedyev's discovery aroused the interest of P. S. Pallas, a Russian academician
travelling in Siberia at that time and it was
subsequently named given his name. The scientist's attention was attracted by the remarkable

structure of this iron boulder. As is known, all pallasites appear to be something like an iron sponge whose pores are filled with the yellow-green mineral olivine. In 1777 Pallas had the meteorite removed to the Kunstkamera of the Petersburg Academy of Sciences where it formed the beginning of the Academy's meteorite collection. Samples of Pallas Iron were then sent to numerous museums throughout the world. In this way they reached Chladni who studied them thoroughly. When Chladni visited Petersburg in 1794 he examined the main mass of Pallas Iron and made a number of additional observations that finally convinced him of its cosmic origin. That same year, in recognition of his outstanding scientific endeavours, Chladni was elected a corresponding member of the Petersburg Academy of Sciences.

However, it was only at the beginning of the Nineteenth Century that meteorites were generally recognized. Meteorite falls began to be considered real natural phenomena only after the publication of a paper by Biot, a member of the Paris Academy, who studied the region and circumstances of a stony meteorite shower which fell on April 26, 1803, near the town L'Aigle in the north of France. Thus, recognition came nearly ten years after publication of Chladni's book containing his conclusions on the cosmic nature of meteorites. Only a few scientists such as Olbers of Germany and Howard of Great Britain supported Chladni's views. A majority of the Scientists in Western Europe regarded Chladni's conclusions dubiously and refused to accept them.

After recognition, meteorites rapidly gained popularity and the interest scientists displayed in them grew steadily. Numerous museums began to collect meteorites and researchers undertook the study of their composition, structure and physical properties. The result was that by the end of the Nineteenth Century great progress had been made in the investigation of meteorites, hundreds of analyses had been performed, data had been obtained on the chemical and mineral

composition of meteorites, new minerals had been
discovered, the specific peculiarities that distinguished meteorites from terrestrial rock were
established and, vica versa, definite features
common to both meteorites and terrestrial rocks
were found. Throughout the last century a large
number of well-known scientists in Russia, Germany, Austria, France, Great Britain, the United
States and other countries engaged in the study
of meteorites. Museums the world over had amas-
sed large meteorite collections.

In speaking of the progress made in the investigation of meteorites, Ju. I. Simashko (1889),
a Russian academician, wrote in 1889 that the
study of meteorites had evolved into an independent domain of science and he suggested that it
be called "meteoritics". This term entered into usage and at the end of the Nineteenth and
beginning of the Twentieth Century a fundamental,
3-volume work by E. Cohen (1894, 1903, 1905) en-
titled "Meteoritenkunde" was published in Germany. In 1915, in the United States, O. C. Farrington (1915) dealt with meteoritics in his
well-known book "Meteorites".

Thus, this new domain of science-meteoritics-
finally established itself in scientific life.
Nevertheless, a generally accepted conception of
the contents, the basic principles and the chief
tasks and aims of this science still remain to
be evolved. The author therefore wishes to present to the reader his views on this score.

Meteoritics should comprise the study of meteoric matter in all its conditions and aspects
and throughout its entire history. One of the
basic tasks of meteoritics consists in the investigation of the relationship between the
Earth as a planet and the meteoric matter present in interplanetary space regardless of its
nature and origin. As far back as 1941, Academician V.I.Vernadsky (1941) pointed out that we
were dealing "with material exchange between our
planet and cosmic space and not with the chance
fall of meteorites, bolides and cosmic dust on
the Earth."

Meteoritics commences with the investigation

of the phenomena accompanying meteorite falls on the earth and proceeds to the study of the conditions of the movement of meteoric bodies in the atmosphere and the processes of their break-up, it determines their original mass and shape and, lastly, it calculates the orbital elements of meteoric bodies in interplanetary space. The above constitute the range of problems that characterize the complex planetary process of interaction between the Earth and interplanetary space surrounding it and determines the place meteorites occupy in the solar system.

Solution of the above tasks in the field of meteoritics is of utmost significance in the solution of the cosmogonic problem of the increase in the Earth's mass due to fall-out of meteoric matter.

In view of the advent of the era of man's conquest of the cosmos, the era of interplanetary communication, investigation of the circumstances of meteorite falls has at present acquired still greater importance.

Meteoritics then proceeds to an overall study of the matter composition, structure and physical properties of meteorites and, in the first place, takes into account the specific features acquired while travelling through the atmosphere at cosmic velocity. After the changes that take place in meteorites have been considered, solution of another cardinal problem, elucidation of the conditions of their formation and determination of the part they play in the planetary system, can be undertaken.

Special mention should be made here of a recently established fact: when studying meteoric matter, in addition to the generally known meteorites, now believed to be fragments of asteroids, matter of a different origin is also encountered. Thus, it has been found that the Tunguska meteorite was the core of a comet and this explains why no solid fragments have been discovered in the area of the fall. Examination of soil samples led to the discovery of dispersed matter that is in all probability is connected with the Tunguska meteorite.

However that may be, there can be no doubt
that the material composition, structure and
physical properties of meteorites reflect the
conditions of their formation and their subsequent history. It will be no exaggeration to
say that a thorough study of the composition and
structure of meteorites bearing traces of long
and unique development will facilitate more rapid, thorough and reliable solution of the question of the composition and nature of the proto-
planetary cloud and its evolution to the very
formation of planets.

In conclusion, it is necessary to mention the
significance of international collaboration in
the sphere of meteoritics.

In view of certain specific features of meteoritics, international cooperation is the only
means of successfully accomplishing a number of
research tasks. This is due to the fact that
meteorites --the subject matter of meteoritics--
fall on the Earth's surface is purely incidental.
Hence certain rare types of meteorites or samples noted for their peculiar composition, structure, morphological and other properties, become
the possession of one museum or another. These
meteorite samples should be studied as thoroughly
as possible from diverse points of view by researchers with differing specialties and with
the employment of methods and apparatus at the
disposal of various research bodies. To accom-
plish this, international cooperation is necessary. It would make meteorite samples available
to researchers participating in a previously
arranged research program.

It would also be of advantage to promote international cooperation in selecting meteoritic matter for chemical analyses to be made according
to definite methods, in the further exploration
of meteoritic craters, in the search for, collection and study of meteoric and cosmic dust,
tektites and silica-glass and other research
work.

The Permanent Commission on Meteorites of the
International Geological Congress and Subcommis-
sion No. 22-a on Meteorites of the International

Astronomical Union are the international bodies
that can organize international cooperation in
the field of meteoritics.

REFERENCES

Chladni, E. F. F. 1794. Uber den Ursprung der
   von Pallas gefundenen und anderer ihr ahnlicher
   Eisenmassen, Riga.
Cohen, E. 1894. Meteoritenkunde, H.1, Stuttgart.
Cohen, E. 1903. Meteoritenkunde, H.2, Stuttgart.
Cohen, E. 1905. Meteoritenkunde, H.3, Stuttgart.
Farrington, O. C. 1915. Meteorites, Chicago.
Krinov, E. L. 1949. Meteoritika, 6, 3-7
Krinov, E. L. 1960. Principles of Meteoritics,
   Pergamon Press, London.
Simashko, Ju. I. 1889. Niva, (3), 61-86; (7), 190-
   195; (12), 314-316.
Vernadsky, V. 1941. Meteoritika, 1, 3-22.

PETER SIGNER

ALFRED O. C. NIER

University of Minnesota

The Measurement and Interpretation

of Rare Gas Concentrations

in Iron Meteorites

The concentrations of He^3 and He^4 have been studied in this laboratory as a function of position in cross sections of the iron meteorites Grant, Carbo, Casas Grandes and Keen Mountain. (Hoffman and Nier, 1958; 1959; 1960) In the case of Grant, a more comprehensive study (Signer and Nier, 1960, 1961) repeated the determinations of He^3 and He^4 and included the isotopes Ne^{20}, Ne^{21}, Ne^{22}, Ar^{36} and Ar^{38} as well. Carbo (Paneth et al, 1952; Fireman, 1958), Sikhote Alin (Vinogradov et al, 1957; Gerling and Levskil, 1958), Treysa (Fechtig, 1960), and Grant (Fireman, 1959) have been investigated in other laboratories. The general purposes of investigations of this type are to learn about the interaction of cosmic rays with meteoroids, the radiation dosage and the ablation of meteoroids in their passage through the earth's atmosphere. The present work reports on the concentrations of the cosmogenic rare gas isotopes in more than 20 iron meteorites. The results are used to deduce information about exposure ages, the sizes of the irradiated bodies and the location of the samples in the bodies.

TABLE I

List of meteorites studied together with individuals who supplied samples and sample identification.

1 Meteorite	2 Analysis Number	3 Source	4 Sample Identification
1 Deep Spring		C. A. Bauer	
2 Clark County		R. Davis, Jr.	Nininger No. 181.11
3 Aroos	S98	M. Honda	Aroos No. 1
	S106	M. Honda	Aroos No. 2
4 Mercedites		P. Gast	fig. 1e
5 Charcas	S27	P. Gast	fig. 1f
	S106		fig. 1f
6 Grant		E. P. Henderson	fig. 1a
7 Williamstown	S85	M. Honda	
	S106	O. A. Schaeffer	N.Y. Mus. of Nat.Hist.
8 Carbo		E. L. Fireman	fig. 1b
9 Keen Mountain		E. P. Henderson	fig. 1h
10 Washington Cy.	S61,S70	E. P. Henderson	
	S135	O. A. Schaeffer	
11 Odessa	S85	M. Honda	Odessa No. 1
	S100	M. Honda	Odessa No. 2
	S97	O. A. Schaeffer	Wards No. 33.20
12 Tocopilla		W. Herr	
13 Sikhote Alin	S26,S80	W. Herr	cut from piece No. 1590
	S78	H. Oeschger	
	S96	O. A. Schaeffer	No. 2052
	S99	M. Honda	Sikhote Alin No. 1
	S121	M. Honda	Sikhote Alin No. 4 fig. 1g
14 Casas Grandes		E. P. Henderson	fig. 1c
15 Admire (Fe-Phase)	S86,S113	M. Honda	
16 Coya Norte		C. A. Bauer	
17 Rio Loa		C. A. Bauer	
18 Toluca		O. A. Schaeffer	Wards No. 221
19 Negrillos		C. A. Bauer	
20 Bethany		W. Herr	
21 Otumpa		M. H. Hey	
22 Willamette		E. P. Henderson	U.S. Nat.Hist.Mus. No.2234
23 Brenham (Fe-Phase)		M. Honda	

EXPERIMENTAL PROCEDURE AND RESULTS

As in the previous work (Signer and Nier, 1960), the samples were completely vaporized in a vacuum chamber. The mixture of the released gases was purified over hot titanium metal and then admitted to the statically operated mass spectrometer. Measurements were put on an absolute basis by calibrating the mass spectrometer with standard samples of rare gas mixtures having a known composition. Whenever sufficient sample material was available at least two independent analyses were made.

Because the concentrations of cosmogenic nuclides depend upon the position of the sample in the irradiated body, it is not a sufficient sample description to give merely the name of the meteorite. Accordingly, Table 1 gives the meteorites investigated, our supplier and, if known, his sample description. Where different samples from the same meteorite were analyzed and their relative geometric positions are known, these positions are shown in Fig. 1.

The results of the analyses of the concentrations of the rare gases are given numerically in Table II and graphically in Fig. 2. The samples are arranged in order of decreasing Ne^{21} concentration. The results of all the individual runs are indicated in order to show the reproducibility and also to illustrate correlations to be discussed in detail below. Where several independent runs were carried out on the same sample, the average is used for further discussions.

The first column of Table II gives the name of the meteorite and the laboratory analysis number. In some cases samples were cut into several pieces and independent analyses made; to distinguish the analyses a letter has been added to the analysis number. In general, different analysis numbers given for the same meteorite indicate that the samples came from different locations in the meteorite. The second column gives the weight of the analyzed material. To show the reproducibility of the procedure, the analysis date is given in the third column.

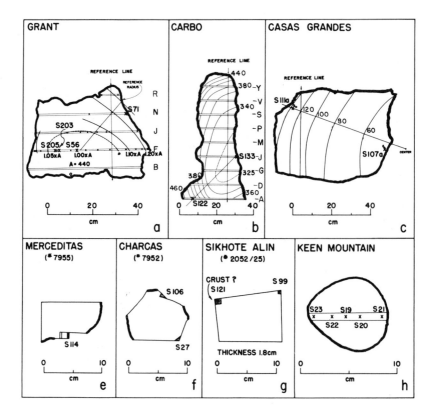

Figure 1.   Sketches showing positions of those
samples where sample locations are known.

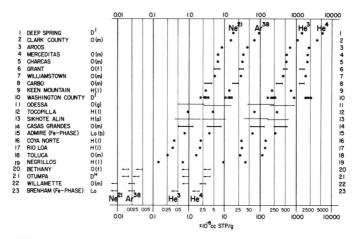

Fig. 2. Concentrations of cosmogenic rare gas nuclides. Values are given on logarithmic scale. Heavy solid lines indicate range of concentrations found when samples from several different known locations in the meteorite were analyzed. Light solid lines indicate range of concentrations when geometric relation between several samples of the same meteorite was not known. In the case of the last four meteorites, the tails of the arrows give the upper limits of concentration. The meteorite classification, in all cases, is given following the name (Leonard and De Violini, 1956). In a private communication, E.P.Henderson describes Aroos as a coarse octahedrite (O (g)).

The concentration of the four cosmogenic isotopes He^3, He^4, Ne^{21} and Ar^{38} are given in units of 10^{-8} cc STP/g in columns 4 through 7. The He^3/He^4 ratios are determined directly and hence are more precise than the ratios computed from the rounded-off figures for the absolute concentrations given in columns 4 and 5. Column 9 gives the Ar^{36}/Ar^{38} ratios. These ratios were

TABLE II: CONCENTRATIONS AND NUCLIDE RATIOS FOR COSMOGENIC RARE GASES IN 23 IRON METEORITES.

Neon values are not corrected for slight amounts of atmospheric neon known to be present in some of the runs. Effect is negligible in case of Ne^{21}. Ar^{38} values are corrected for atmospheric argon assuming all the Ar^{40} is of atmospheric origin. Helium values do not require correction for atmospheric helium.

1	2	3	4	5	6	7	8	9	10	11	12	13	14	15	16	17
Meteorite and Analysis No.	Wt. mg	Date of Measurement	He^3 $\times 10^8$ cc STP/g	He^4	Ne^{21}	Ar^{38}	$\dfrac{He^3}{He^4}$	$\dfrac{Ar^{36}}{Ar^{38}}$	$\dfrac{Ar^{40}}{Ar^{38}}$	$\dfrac{Ne^{20}}{Ne^{21}}$	$\dfrac{Ne^{22}}{Ne^{21}}$	$\dfrac{He^3}{Ne^{21}}$	$\dfrac{He^3}{Ar^{38}}$	$\dfrac{He^4}{Ne^{21}}$	$\dfrac{He^4}{Ar^{38}}$	$\dfrac{Ne^{21}}{Ar^{38}}$
1 Deep Spring S102a	175	10/ 3/60	1470	5470	17.6	89.5	0.268	0.645	1.5	1.02	1.04					
S102b	94.4	9/22/60	1460	5450	17.8	90.5	0.268	0.655	1.5	1.07	1.04					
Average S102			1465	5460	17.7	90.0	0.268	0.650				83.0	16.3	310	60.5	0.195
2 Clark County S101a	226	9/ 8/60	1090	3760	15.4	69.0	0.290	0.660	6.6	1.10	1.05					
S101b	252	10/ 3/60	1090	3850	15.2	69.0	0.283	0.660	2.5	1.05	1.04					
S101c	156	10/11/60	1105	3860	15.1	68.0	0.285	0.650	2.1	1.01	1.04					
Average S101			1095	3820	15.2	69.0	0.286	0.655				72.0	15.9	250	55.5	0.220
3 Aroos S 98b	265	9/23/60	660	2550	8.25	44.0	0.258	0.650	3.4	1.03	1.04					
S 98c	360	9/29/60	650	2520	8.10	43.0	0.258	0.645	4.3	1.05	1.04					
S 98d	227	10/ 3/60	660	2560	8.05	43.5	0.259	0.640	3.9	1.05	1.05					
Average S 98			655	2540	8.15	43.5	0.258	0.645				80.5	15.1	310	58.5	0.185
S104a	369	10/ 6/60	655	2520	8.20	42.5	0.260	0.640	2.8	1.05	1.05					
S104b	200	10/10/60	655	2510	8.10	42.5	0.261	0.640	1.9	1.04	1.05					
Average S104			655	2510	8.15	42.5	0.260	0.640				80.5	15.4	310	59.0	0.190
4 Mercedites S114a	513	11/ 1/60	545	2060	6.55	34.5	0.266	0.645	5.3	1.12	1.05					
S114b	395	11/11/60	530	1990	6.45	32.5	0.265	0.645	3.3	1.07	1.05					
S114c	196	12/ 6/60	545	2060	6.60	35.0	0.265	0.645	9.2	1.20	1.05					
Average S114			540	2040	6.55	34.0	0.265	0.645				82.5	16.0	310	60.0	0.195

12

1	2	3	4	5	6	7	8	9	10	11	12	13	14	15	16	17
Meteorite and Analysis No.	Wt. mg	Date of Measurement	He^3	He^4	Ne^{21}	Ar^{38}	$\frac{He^3}{He^4}$	$\frac{Ar^{36}}{Ar^{38}}$	$\frac{Ar^{40}}{Ar^{38}}$	$\frac{Ne^{20}}{Ne^{21}}$	$\frac{Ne^{22}}{Ne^{21}}$	$\frac{He^3}{Ne^{21}}$	$\frac{He^3}{Ar^{38}}$	$\frac{He^4}{Ne^{21}}$	$\frac{He^4}{Ar^{38}}$	$\frac{Ne^{21}}{Ar^{38}}$
			$\times 10^8$ cc STP/g													
5 Charcas S 27	326	1/22/59	530	1980	6.30	33.5	0.266	0.630	0.65	1.02	1.06	84.0	16.0	315	59.0	0.190
S106a	246	10/10/60	535	2030	6.80	33.0	0.265	0.645	2.4	1.02	1.05					
S106b	221	11/ 4/60	540	2040	6.65	36.5	0.263	0.650	1.4	1.05	1.04					
S106c	196	12/ 4/60	540	2040	6.75	34.5	0.265	0.650	9.8	1.18	1.05					
Average S106			540	2040	6.75	34.5	0.264	0.650				80.0	15.5	300	59.0	0.195
6 Grant Center S 56a	275	5/ 1/59	450	1785	5.25	27.0	0.252	0.620	1.25	1.03	1.05					
S 56b	442	5/ 1/59	435	1770	5.05	26.5	0.245	0.620	0.52	0.99	1.05					
Average S 56			440	1780	5.15	27.0	0.248	0.620				85.5	16.5	345	66.0	0.190
Bar F-238 S203	209	12/ 6/60	440	1770	5.30	28.5	0.249	0.635	11	1.20	1.07	83.0	15.5	335	62.0	0.185
Bar F-246 S205	198	12/ 6/60	450	1780	5.35	28.0	0.250	0.635	10	1.24	1.07	84.0	16.0	335	63.5	0.190
Surface S 71a	184	8/18/59	550	1990	7.45	34.5	0.276	0.640	1.44	1.05	1.07	74.0	16.0	265	57.5	0.215
7 Williamstown S 85a	362	10/21/59	465	1800	5.20	25.0	0.258	0.630	7.7	1.04	1.05					
S 85b	263	9/27/60	465	1800	5.35	29.5	0.257	0.645	27	1.54	1.10					
Average S 85			465	1800	5.30	27.0	0.258	0.635				87.5	17.0	340	66.5	0.195
S105a	417	10/ 6/60	475	1830	5.40	30.0	0.257	0.635	2.1	1.03	1.04					
S105b	260	11/11/60	450	1770	5.10	28.5	0.255	0.635	7.9	1.21	1.06					
Average S105			460	1800	5.25	29.0	0.256	0.635				87.5	16.0	340	62.0	0.180
8 Carbo Center S133	171	11/25/60	280	1220	2.80	17.0	0.232	0.625	5.3	1.17	1.05	100	16.5	435	71.5	0.165
Surface S122a	129	11/18/60	410	1690	4.50	24.5	0.241	0.630	1.5	1.07	1.05					
S122b	109	11/18/60	405	1680	4.35	25.0	0.242	0.630	1.9	1.10	1.04					
Average S122			410	1685	4.40	25.0	0.242	0.630				93.0	16.5	385	67.4	0.185

13

1	2	3	4	5	6	7	8	9	10	11	12	13	14	15	16	17
Meteorite and Analysis No.	Wt. (mg)	Date of Measurement	He^3	He^4	Ne^{21}	Ar^{38}	$\frac{He^3}{He^4}$	$\frac{Ar^{36}}{Ar^{38}}$	$\frac{Ar^{40}}{Ar^{38}}$	$\frac{Ne^{20}}{Ne^{21}}$	$\frac{Ne^{22}}{Ne^{21}}$	$\frac{He^3}{Ne^{21}}$	$\frac{He^3}{Ar^{38}}$	$\frac{He^4}{Ne^{21}}$	$\frac{He^4}{Ar^{38}}$	$\frac{Ne^{21}}{Ar^{38}}$
			$\times 10^8$ cc STP/g													
9 Keen Mountain S 21	262	1/ 2/59	205	735	2.80	13.5	0.275	0.635	1.6	1.02	1.08					
S 20	305	12/31/58	205	755	2.85	13.5	0.271	0.630	1.3	1.01	1.09					
S 19	399	12/29/58	215	775	2.95	13.0	0.280	0.630	1.1	1.01	1.08					
S 22	305	1/ 5/59	215	770	3.00	13.5	0.278	0.630	0.8	1.00	1.08					
S 23	256	1/13/59	220	780	3.05	14.0	0.280	0.640	1.1	1.05	1.08					
Average S 19-S23			210	760	2.95	13.5	0.277	0.630				71.0	15.5	260	56.5	0.220
10 Washington Co. S 61**	353	5/28/59	205	2180	2.77	13.5	0.095	0.640	1.5	2.12	1.12	74.0	15.0	790	160	0.205
S 70a**	356	8/20/59	225	1810	2.94	14.5	0.117	0.635	3.3	1.85	1.11	76.5	15.5	620	125	0.205
S 70b**	380	12/20/60	165	870	2.12	10.5	0.192	0.640	5.1	1.24	1.06	78.0	15.5	410	83	0.200
S135a	318	12/20/60	265	2570	3.52	16.0	0.102	0.655	4.4	2.00	1.10	75.5	16.5	730	160	0.220
S135b	435	12/20/60	225	1930	2.90	14.0	0.116	0.650	4.3	1.81	1.09	77.5	16.0	670	140	0.205
11 Odessa S 83	425	10/29/59	44.5	185	0.478	2.60	0.242	0.620	18	1.37	1.08	93.0	17.0	395	73.0	0.185
S100a	470	9/ 8/60	114	450	1.29	7.40	0.252	0.630	31	1.62	1.09					
S100b	345	9/19/60	94.0	380	1.09	6.20	0.247	0.640	37	1.70	1.10					
S100c	411	9/22/60	101	405	1.09	6.60	0.248	0.650	22	1.39	1.09					
Average S100			103	415	1.16	6.75	0.249	0.640	33	1.58	1.09	89.0	15.5	360	61.5	0.170
S 97b	256	9/ 8/60	235	920	2.77	15.0	0.257	0.640				85.5	15.5	330	61.5	0.185
12 Tocopilla S115	312	10/31/60	68.5	295	0.92	4.70	0.231	0.650	80	2.95	1.24	74.5	14.5	320	63.0	0.195
13 Sikhote Alin S 26a	312	1/19/59	37.0	160	0.385	2.25	0.230	0.605	11	1.38	1.11					
S 78b	416	8/ 6/59	37.0	160	0.405	2.40	0.230	0.610	12	1.42	1.07					
S 80a	295	8/ 6/59	39.5	170	0.400	2.40	0.232	0.610	23	1.53	1.08					
Average S 26**, S78**, S 80**			38.0	165	0.400	2.35	0.231	0.610				94.0	16.0	410	70.0	0.170

** Adjacent samples.

14

1	2	3	4	5	6	7	8	9	10	11	12	13	14	15	16	17
Meteorite and Analysis No.	Wt.	Date of Measurement	He^3	He^4	Ne^{21}	Ar^{38}	$\frac{He^3}{He^4}$	$\frac{Ar^{36}}{Ar^{38}}$	$\frac{Ar^{40}}{Ar^{38}}$	$\frac{Ne^{20}}{Ne^{21}}$	$\frac{Ne^{22}}{Ne^{21}}$	$\frac{He^3}{Ne^{21}}$	$\frac{He^3}{Ar^{38}}$	$\frac{He^4}{Ne^{21}}$	$\frac{He^4}{Ar^{38}}$	$\frac{Ne^{21}}{Ar^{38}}$
	mg		$\times 10^8$ cc STP/g													
S 96a	288	6/16/60	115	480	1.30	7.15	0.240	0.635	19	1.45	1.10					
S 96b	473	9/ 6/60	125	495	1.35	8.10	0.247	0.635	26	1.54	1.09					
Average S 96			120	490	1.35	7.60	0.244	0.635				89.0	16.0	365	64.5	0.180
S 99a	348	9/ 6/60	160	620	2.15	10.5	0.260	0.645	28	1.48	1.09					
S 99b	450	9/19/60	160	620	2.10	10.5	0.263	0.645	11	1.17	1.06					
Average S 99			160	620	2.10	10.5	0.262	0.645				76.0	15.0	295	59.0	0.200
S121a	617	11/11/60	170	625	2.15	10.5	0.271	0.645	2.4	1.05	1.05					
S121b	418	12/18/60	170	630	2.20	10.5	0.268	0.645	6.3	1.15	1.03					
Average S121			170	630	2.20	10.5	0.270	0.645				77.5	16.0	285	60.0	0.210
14 Casas Grandes Center S107a=E	311	10/18/60	54.0	245	0.515	3.25	0.220	0.620	33	1.83	1.12	105	16.5	475	75.5	0.160
Surface S111a=B10	310	10/21/60	133	560	1.38	8.30	0.238	0.630	14	1.34	1.08	96.5	16.0	405	67.5	0.165
15 Admire S 86a	242	10/21/59	63.0	270	0.760	4.10	0.232	0.635	25	1.68	1.12					
S 86b	715	9/26/60	58.5	245	0.790	3.70	0.232	0.650	121	3.1	1.25					
S113	396	10/31/60	65.5	285	1.78*	3.75	0.230	0.640	310	4.05	1.32					
Average S86,S113			62.5	270	0.775	3.85	0.231	0.640				80.5	16.0	350	70.0	0.200
16 Coya Norte S119	673	11/10/60	30.0	144	0.385	2.20	0.210	0.630	24	1.64	1.05	78.0	13.5	375	65.5	0.175
17 Rio Loa S118	708	11/ 3/60	31.5	140	0.360	2.10	0.226	0.625	46	2.10	1.14	87.5	15.0	390	66.5	0.170

* High value probably due to stone inclusion.

15

1	2	3	4	5	6	7	8	9	10	11	12	13	14	15	16	17
Meteorite and Analysis No.	Wt. mg	Date of Measurement	He^3	He^4	Ne^{21}	Ar^{38}	$\dfrac{He^3}{He^4}$	$\dfrac{Ar^{36}}{Ar^{38}}$	$\dfrac{Ar^{40}}{Ar^{38}}$	$\dfrac{Ne^{20}}{Ne^{21}}$	$\dfrac{Ne^{22}}{Ne^{21}}$	$\dfrac{He^3}{Ne^{21}}$	$\dfrac{He^3}{Ar^{38}}$	$\dfrac{He^4}{Ne^{21}}$	$\dfrac{He^4}{Ar^{38}}$	$\dfrac{Ne^{21}}{Ar^{38}}$
			$\times 10^8$ cc STP/g													
18 Toluca S 95a	273	6/16/60	29.0	116	0.255	1.60	0.227	0.640	76	2.55	1.18					
S 95b	249	9/ 6/60	28.0	122	0.250	1.70	0.227	0.650	41	5.50	1.41					
Average S 95			28.5	119	0.250	1.65	0.227	0.645				114	17.5	475	72.0	0.150
19 Negrillos S120	672	11/ 7/60	9.6	40	0.14	0.69	0.24	0.650	45	2.15	1.16	69	14	285	58	0.20
20 Otumpa S103	388	9/25/60	≤1	≤4	≤0.01	≤0.04										
21 Willamette S117	444	11/ 3/60	≤1	≤3	≤0.02	≤0.03										
22 Bethany S116	508	11/ 3/60	≤1	≤4	≤0.02	≤0.05										
23 Brenham S 84	373	10/12/59	≤0.5	≤2	≤0.01	≤0.03										

16

corrected assuming that all the Ar^{40} observed was of atmospheric origin. The magnitude of this correction may be seen from the Ar^{40}/Ar^{38} ratios given in column 10. It is to be noted that in order to save time less care was taken in outgassing the extraction system and sample surfaces than in the work on Grant reported earlier; thus, in general, these ratios are higher. Likewise a corresponding atmospheric neon contamination resulted in the slightly higher measured Ne^{20}/Ne^{21} and Ne^{22}/Ne^{21} ratios (see columns 11 and 12). Experience has shown that for atmospheric contamination the Ne/Ar ratio lies in the range 1/1000 to 1/500. If a correction of this magnitude is applied to the ratios given in columns 11 and 12, then, except for the Washington County, all the resulting values agree with the cosmogenic values, 0.96 ± 0.05 and 1.05 ± 0.04, found for Ne^{20}/Ne^{21} and Ne^{22}/Ne^{21} in Grant.

In Fig. 2 the concentration of Ne^{21}, Ar^{38}, He^{3} and He^{4} as given in Table II are plotted graphically. Note the logarithmic scale for the detected concentrations. In those cases where samples of known relative location within the meteorite were available (Grant, Carbo and Casas Grandes), the two extreme concentrations were plotted for each isotope and connected with a heavily solid line. The ranges of the different samples of Sikhote Alin and Odessa are given by a thin line (geometric relationship not known). For Washington County, where the spread of the results has to be explained differently than by depth variations, all individual analyses are plotted. The generally parallel trend of the four concentrations (in the logerithmic graph) makes evident that no drastic variations of any nuclide ratio occurs, in spite of concentration variations between samples of more than two orders of magnitude.

Nevertheless significant variations beyond the errors in measurement, 7 to 10%, do exist as may be seen from columns 13 to 17 in Table II. Even without including Washington County, the He^{4}/Ne^{21} ratio shows the largest variation.

Smaller variations, definitely beyond the limits of error, are exhibited by He^3/Ne^{21} and Ne^{21}/Ar^{38}. He^3/Ar^{38} varies the least--barely exceeding the limits of error. This latter result disagrees with the measurements of Schaeffer and Zahringer (1960), who found this ratio to vary by a factor of more than three among different meteorites. This discrepancy is of some importance since the presumed variation is an essential part of a method proposed and used (Fisher and Schaeffer, 1960; Fisher, 1961c) for determining exposure ages.

DISCUSSION

A. Production Mechanism

The fact that rare gases in iron meteorites are produced predominantly by the interaction of cosmic radiation with the meteoritic matter provides means for studying the history of meteorites as well as cosmic rays. In order to study these phenomena on more than a qualitative basis, it is necessary to postulate some model for the interaction mechanism. In the previous study of Grant (Signer and Nier, 1960), it was shown that the model proposed by Martin (1953) and Ebert and Wanke (1957) gave a satisfactory understanding of the experimental results. It is assumed that the rays passing through the meteoritic body can be considered to consist of two groups, primaries with average energies of several Bev., and low energy secondaries. One assigns an unique interaction cross section to each group and an energy independent production cross section for each rare gas isotope. If the primary radiation contains a relatively large number of particles with energies below 1 Bev. (Wanke, 1960b), the formulation will become more complex. Actually this difficulty may not be too serious since in practice the outer part of the meteorites, in which one would expect to find the effects of the low energy primaries, are ablated during the passage through the atmosphere. Furthermore, the cosmogenic rare gases, especially

the Ne and Ar are predominantly produced by interaction of particles of higher energies.

The cross sections for the production of the
various rare gas nuclides have been found (Hoffman and Nier, 1958; Signer and Nier, 1960)
from the empirically determined parameters in
the production equation. It would be highly
desirable to measure these cross sections directly in laboratory experiments and attempts
in this direction have been made (Fireman and
Zahringer, 1957; Schaeffer and Zahringer, 1959;
Goebel and Zahringer, 1961). However, the results are incomplete and subject to question in-
asmuch as the bombardment conditions (the part
played by scattered particles for example) inside a meteorite may be quite different than for
either a long or a thin target exposed to a beam
in an accelerator.

In spite of its obvious over-simplification,
the model has been reasonably successful in providing a semi-quantative explanation of experimental results. Further comparisons are in order, first of all, as a means of understanding
the amounts and distribution of cosmogenic nuclides found in meteorites and secondly, to obtain guidance on how the model might be improved.

In the analysis of Grant, certain assumptions
were made. These must be borne in mind as applications are made. The assumptions were:

(a) The formula proposed by Ebert and Wanke
     (1957) is adequate to describe the produc-
     tion of cosmogenic Ne, Ar and even He in
     iron meteorites.

(b) Grant can be considered as having been a
     spherical meteoroid and the variation of
     He^3, He^4, Ne^{21} and Ar^{38} determined along
     the reference radius chosen is represen-
     tative.

(c) The size of the meteroid did not change
     during the exposure to cosmic rays.

(d) The intensity and energy spectrum of the
     galactic cosmic radiation did not change
     during the exposure of the meteoroid.

(e) The effects of the fluctuations of solar
     cosmic radiation may be neglected.

In principle these assumptions enable one to compute the concentrations of He^3, He^4, Ne^{21} and Ar^{38} at any location in iron meteoroids of any size, shape and exposure age. Conversely a knowledge of these concentrations at a sufficient number of points in a meteroid can be used to determine the size, shape and exposure age as well as the concentrations at any arbitrary location in the body. In the special case where the meteoroid can be considered as spherical, the measurement of the He^3, He^4, Ne^{21} and Ar^{38} concentrations at a single point allows one to determine the location of the sample in the body and also the size of the meteoroid and its exposure age.

B.   Relationship between Concentrations of Cosmogenic Rare Gasses

The functional relationship between the several nuclides in spherical meteoroids can be presented in a number of different ways. One method is to plot the He^4/Ar^{38} ratio against He^3/Ne^{21} as was done in Fig. 3. Curves computed from the production formula using the Grant data are shown for meteoroids having masses of 2×10^3, 2×10^4, and 2×10^5 kg. The open triangles indicate measurements on meteorites where only a single sample was available. The other symbols correspond to measurements on meteorites as indicated where two or more samples were available. In some cases the geometric relationship between the samples was known, in others not.

Except for Washington County all the measurements fall within or close to the band of values allowed for by the experimental errors assigned to the curves. The striking disparity for this meteorite suggests the existence of an anomaly, i.e. an unusual source for one or more of the isotopes (Schaeffer and Fisher, 1960a). With this exception, the meteorites investigated here appear to be remarkably "normal". This is in contrast to the observations of Fisher and Schaeffer (1960), who reported eight cases out of fifteen where one or more isotope appeared to be anomalous.

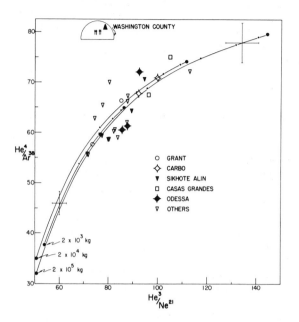

Fig. 3. Curves showing variation of He^4/Ar^{38} with He^3/Ne^{21} in spherical iron meteorites having masses of 2×10^3, 2×10^4 and 2×10^5 kg. Surface points lie at left ends of curves, centers at right. Points on curves correspond to fractional distances from center of 0.2, 0.4, 0.6 and 0.8. The large crosses near the ends of the curves show the effect of a 5 percent error in the determination of the relative concentrations. Experimental results listed in Table II are plotted.

C. Relationships between Concentration and Size, Depth, and Exposure Age

In Fig. 3 one plots the ratio of the concentrations of two cosmogenic nuclides against the ratio of the concentrations of two others. Thus exposure age does not enter. On the other hand, if one plots the concentration of a single nu-

clide against the ratio of two other nuclides as
as was done in Fig. 11 of Signer and Nier (1960),
the position of a point depends upon exposure
age as well as upon the relative depth of a sample and the size of the meteoroid.

Heymann and Schaeffer (1961) have measured the
specific activity of Cl^{36} in Grant. This measurement combined with the average Ar^{36} concentration
reported for Grant (Signer and Nier, 1960) en-
abled them to compute an exposure age of close
to 600 my. If one accepts this age, the abscissa
scale of Fig. 11, (Signer and Nier (1960) can
be changed from Ar^{38} concentration to Ar^{38} production rate. This has been done in Fig. 4.
Assuming, one knows the size of a spherical meteoroid and the concentrations of He^3, Ne^{21} and
Ar^{38} in a single sample from an unknown position
in the meteoroid, Fig. 4 permits one to determine the relative depth of the sample and the
production rate of Ar^{38}. With this latter quantity and the measured Ar^{38} concentration, the
exposure age can be computed.

Unfortunately, in practice, the pre-atmospheric
size of meteoritic bodies are not known. Thus
in evaluating the Ar^{38} production from Fig. 4,
one does not know which of the heavy curves to
employ, and therefore, additional information is
needed. The knowledge of the concentration of
another cosmogenic nuclide, such as He^4, provides this information. A graph similar to
Fig. 4, but employing He^3, He^4 and Ar^{38}, can be
drawn. This has been done in Fig. 5. Since
data for four nuclides are available, two additional independent combinations of three nuclides
out of the four are possible, leading to two
additional graphs (for example, Ne^{21} vs He^4/Ar^{38}
and Ne^{21} vs He^3/He^4). In the interest of brevi-
ty these are not shown. In principle, a simul-
taneous consideration of two graphs such as
Figs. 4 and 5 make possible a unique determination of the size of meteoroid, the relative
depth and the exposure age. In practice, experimental errors and the failure of conditions to
approach the ideal assumed makes it highly desirable, if not essential, to consider all four
graphs.

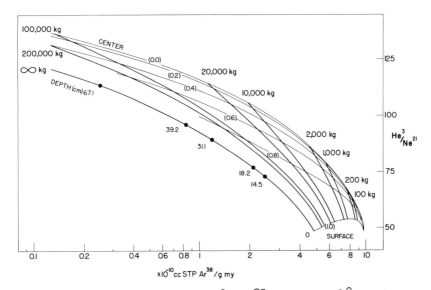

Fig. 4.   Variation of He^3/Ne^{21} with Ar^{38} production rate as a function of position in spherical meteoroids of various sizes as computed from production equation and the analysis of Grant (Signer and Nier, 1960).   To obtain the Argon production rate, the exposure age of Grant has been taken as 600 my (Heymann and Schaeffer, 1961).   The heavy curves show the relationship for spherical meteoids having various masses. The light curves show the relationship for various relative distances from the center (r/R = 0.0, 0.2, 0.4, 0.6, 0.8, 1.0).   The dots on the infinitely large meteorite curve correspond to values found at depths equal to the radii of 10^2, 2 x 10^2, 10^3, 2 x 10^3 and 10^4 kg. meteoroids (reading from right to left on the curve).

The conclusions based on considerations of the type stated above are listed in Table III for 19 of the 23 meteorites investigated.   Column 3 gives the pre-atmospheric mass of the spherical meteorite (to help visualize the size, the corresponding radius is also shown).   Column 4

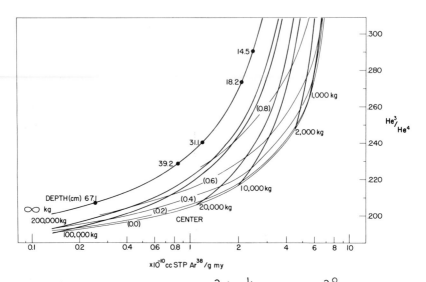

Fig. 5. Variation of He^3/He^4 with Ar^{38} production rate plotted in a manner analogous to Fig. 4.

indicates the depth of the sample, expressing this as the ratio of the sample's distance from the center of the spherical body to its pre-atmospheric radius. The range of values given reflects the uncertainty of the conclusions drawn from the different graphs. Column 5 shows the exposure ages deduced. Again, the uncertainty is indicated by the stated errors.

Columns 6 through 9 indicate the production rates of cosmogenic He^3, He^4, Ne^{21} and Ar^{38} as found from the concentrations of these nuclides and the ages given in column 5. Within a single column one notes variations of as much as an order of magnitude. These are attributed to the differences in shielding. Urey (1959) has used a He^3 production rate of 50 x 10^{-10} cc STP per gram million years in estimating the exposure ages of some iron meteorites from their He^3 concentrations. This rate falls well within the extremities of the range of values deduced here.

In the study of Grant, a comparison of concentration ratios between surface and center for the several nuclides shows that the variation is greatest for Ne^{21}; that is Ne^{21} is the most depth sensitive. The percentage variations of He^3 and Ar^{38} are approximately the same but less than that of Ne^{21}. The He^4 variation is still less. the same general behavior is noted for the samples listed in Table III. These observations are in disagreement with the variations of production rates deduced by Fisher and Schaeffer (1960), who indicate that Ar^{38} exhibits the greatest variation, with that for Ne^{21} falling between that for Ar^{38} and He^3.

In an analysis of eight chondrites, Geiss et al (1960) showed a remarkable grouping of the He^3-T ages. Heymann and Schaeffer (1961) determined Ar^{36}-Cl^{36} ages in four iron meteorites and found three of the ages to lie near 600 my and one near 250 my. Of the 19 meteorites listed in Table III 16 appear to lie near one of these two values. Whether it is significant or not, it is interesting to note that most of the octahedrites fall in the older group whereas most of the hexahedrites fall in the younger group. Bauer (1961) has studied the helium in a number of meteorites and shown that in general the He concentration in octahedrites is higher than in hexahedrites and Ni-poor ataxites. The measurements of Schaeffer and Zahringer (1960) and Fisher and Schaeffer (1960) show the same tendency.

D. Exposure Age Comparisons

Several of the meteorites investigated in the present work have been analyzed for cosmogenic radioisotopes in other laboratories. Of particular interest in Cl^{36} which permits calculation of exposure ages by the Ar^{36}-Cl^{36} method. It should be noted that in the case of unobserved falls the Ar^{36}-Cl^{36} exposure age may be affected substantially by a decay of Cl^{36} between the unknown time of fall and the present. Some evidence for such a decay exists in the case of the meteorite Williamstown, which exhibits rare gas

TABLE III

Conclusions based on the production model and the rare gas concentrations given in Table II.

	1	2	3		4	5	6	7	8	9
	Meteorite	Recovered Mass	Preatmospheric Mass	Radius	$\frac{r}{R}$	Exposure Age	He^3	He^4	Ne^{21}	Ar^{38}
								Production Rates		
		kg	kg	cm		my	$\times 10^{10}$ cc STP/g my			
1	Deep Spring	11.5	1000	31	0 –0.3	$1500^+_- 100$	100	350	1.2	6.0
2	Clark County	11.3	1000	31	0.5–0.7	$1000^+_- 100$	110	330	1.5	6.9
3	Aroos	150	2000	39	0.4–0.6	$800^+_- 150$	82	320	1.0	5.4
4	Merceditas	42.8	2000	39	0.4–0.5	$600^+_- 150$	90	340	1.1	6.5
5	Charcas	780	2000	39	0.4–0.6	$600^+_- 150$	90	340	1.1	5.7
6	Grant Center	480			0 –0.2		73	300	0.85	4.5
	Surface		2000	39	0.5–0.7	600	92	330	1.2	5.7
7	Williamstown	30.8	2000	39	0 –0.4	$650^+_- 100$	71	280	0.80	4.3
8	Carbo Center	454	6000	57	0	$600^+_- 150$	47	200	0.45	2.9
	Surface				0.4		68	280	0.75	4.1
9	Keen Mountain	6.7	1000	31	0.4–0.7	$200^+_- 50$	105	380	1.5	6.8
10	Washington Cy.	5.8	1000	31	0.2–0.5	$200^+_- 50$				
11	Odessa S 83	Very Big	200000	182	0.7–0.8		10	42	0.11	0.58
	S100				0.8–0.9	$450^+_- 300$	23	92	0.26	1.7
	S 97				0.8–0.9		53	200	0.62	3.4

26

1	2	3		4	5	6	7	8	9
Meteorite	Recovered Mass kg	Preatmospheric Mass kg	Radius cm	L/R	Exposure Age my	He³ ×10¹⁰ cc STP/g	He⁴ (Production Rates ×10¹⁰ cc STP/g my)	Ne²¹	Ar³⁸
12 Tocopilla	75	200000	182	0.8-0.9	250⁺₋100	27	120	0.37	1.9
13 Sikhote Alin S26,S78,S80				0.7-0.8		13	55	0.13	0.78
S96				0.8-0.9		40	160	0.45	2.5
S99	30000	200000	182	0.9	300⁺₋200	54	210	0.70	3.5
S121				0.9		56	210	0.73	3.5
14 Casas Grandes Center	1550	10000	67	0 -0.3	250⁺₋100	22	100	0.20	1.3
Surface				0.4-0.6		53	220	0.55	3.3
15 Admire	50	2000	39	0.3-0.7	150⁺₋50	41	180	0.51	2.5
16 Coya Norte	17.9	200000	182	0.6-0.9	250⁺₋200	12	58	0.15	0.88
17 Rio Loa	4	200000	182	0.8-0.9	150⁺₋50	21	94	0.24	1.4
18 Toluca	20000	200000	182	0.5-0.7	250⁺₋150	11	48	0.10	0.66
19 Negrillos	28.5	200000	182	0.8-0.9	30⁺₋15	32	130	0.47	2.3

concentrations very similar to those found for
Grant and for Carbo. Honda, Shedlovsky and
Arnold (1961) investigated the Be^{10}, Al^{26}, K^{40}
and Mn^{53} activities in the Williamstown and Grant
meteorites and found the respective radioactivities to agree within 20 percent. On the other
hand, Sprenkel (1959) gives the Cl^{36} activity of
Williamstown as only one-fourth that found by
Heymann and Schaeffer (1961) in Grant, the respective figures being 3.3 and 12.4 dpm/kg. This
strongly indicates that Williamstown fell approximately 6×10^5 years earlier than Grant (half-
life of Cl^{36} assumed to be 3.1×10^5y), since
such a difference cannot be explained as due to
different shielding. A parallel situation may
exist for Carbo if the Cl^{36} activity of 3.6 dpm/
kg measured by Sprenkel (1959) is verified.

For some of the other meteorites investigated
here, exposure ages determined by the $Ar^{36}-Cl^{36}$
or $Ar^{38}-Ar^{39}$ method are available. Furthermore,
estimates of the exposure ages of some iron meteorites were given by Hoffman and Nier (1960)
and Fisher and Schaeffer (1960; 1961c). Those
meteorites of Table III for which a comparison
between the present and earlier work is possible
are listed in Fig. 6. The range of exposure age
as computed from the production model used here
is indicated by a solid line. The circles and
the square indicate exposure ages determined by
the $Ar^{36}-Cl^{36}$ and $Ar^{38}-Ar^{39}$ method respectively
whereas the triangles and crosses indicate the
estimates of Hoffman and Nier (1960) and Fisher
and Schaeffer (1960; 1961c) respectively. The
present results, except for Williamstown and
Carbo, are in fair agreement with the directly
determined ages. As has already been mentioned,
for these two meteorites the reliability of the
$Ar^{36}-Cl^{36}$ age seems doubtful. Whether the
spread of $Ar^{36}-Cl^{36}$ exposure ages for Sikhote
Alin is of any significance or is due to experimental difficulty needs further investigation.

For Grant and Keen Mountain, the present results agree well with those of Hoffman and Nier
(1960) (triangles in Fig. 6) based on essentially the same method but employing only He^3 and

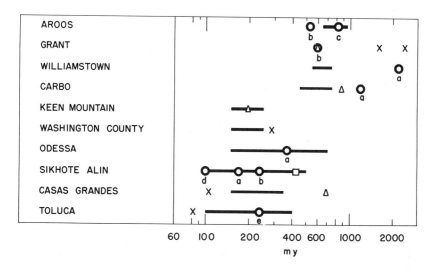

Fig. 6.   Comparison of exposure ages estimated
from present work with other estimates and with
directly determined values. The letters associated with the Ar^{36}-Cl^{36} ages (circles) refer to
the date used in the computations, as follows:
a:(Fisher and Schaeffer, 1960); b: (Heymann and
Schaeffer, 1961); c: Cl^{36}, (Honda and Arnold,
1961) and Ar^{36} from present work; d: Cl^{36},
(Gfeller et al, 1959) and Ar^{36} from present work;
e: Cl^{36}, from (Sprenkle, 1959) and Ar^{36} from
present work. Ar^{38}-Ar^{39} age represented by
square is from Fireman and De Felice (1960)

He^4. For Carbo and Casas Grandes their values
are higher due to the assumption of greater pre-
atmospheric masses. The present values seem
preferable since they are based on concentration
measurements of four rather than two nuclides.
   The age estimates by Fisher and Schaeffer
(1960) and Fisher (1961c), based on the depth
dependence of He^3/Ar^{38} and calibrated by some
directly measured exposure ages, mainly Ar^{36}-Cl^{36},

are indicated by crosses in Fig. 6. For Washington County, Casas Grandes and Toluca there is fair agreement with the present results. For Grant, Fisher (1961c) gives a value more than three times the Ar^{36}-Cl^{36} age given by Heymann and Schaeffer (1961) and adopted in the present paper. In the method of Fisher and Schaeffer, the Ar^{36}-Cl^{36} ages of Williamstown and Carbo which, as previously discussed may be doubtful, enter the production rate calculations in a critical manner. Furthermore, the method depends upon the existence of a variation in the He^3/Ar^{38} ratio determined by the amount of shielding of the sample. According to Table 4 in their publication (Fisher and Schaeffer, 1960) the He^3/Ar^{38} ratio shows larger variations than other rare gas nuclide ratios. This is contrary to all measurements reported both here and previously (Signer and Nier, 1960) and has also been questioned by Wanke (1960a). It appears that a careful reconsideration of the method is necessary.

E. The Washington County Anomalies

The Washington County meteorite, which has been excluded in most of the previous discussion warrants special attention. Schaeffer and Fisher (1960a) reported a low He^3/He^4 ratio for this meteorite, due to an unusually high concentration of He^4. The low ratio has been verified in the present investigation and two further anomalies were observed. These consist of exceptionally high concentrations of Ne^{20} and Ne^{22}, and remarkable variations in concentrations of rare gas nuclides, even between adjacent samples (see Table II). Assuming all the Ar^{40} is atmospheric contamination and that there is an accompanying neon contamination, one can correct the Ne concentration for this contamination according to the relation $Ne^{20}_{atm.} = 0.002\ Ar^{40}_{atm.}$. After such a correction, a significant Ne^{20} concentration excess remains, which is without any doubt incorporated in the sample. If one assumed the cosmogenic He^3/He^4 ratio to be 0.25 and all of the He^3 to be cosmogenic, then the He^4 excess can be computed. An examination of the excess Ne^{20} and excess He^4 shows that, although the amount of excess varies by a factor of five between samples, the ratio $He^4_{excess}/Ne^{20}_{excess}$ remains constant at 420 ± 40. The constancy of this ratio appears significant and makes it difficult to account for the excess He^4 as predominantly of radiogenic origin.

The excess He^4 and Ne could be of either terrestrial or primordial origin; in both cases the ratio would not be unreasonable. For a terrestrial origin, in order to accumulate the measured concentration by inward diffusion from the atmosphere, an elevated temperature would be required. The inward flow of atmospheric gases would be accompanied by an outward diffusion of cosmogenic gases. For comparison it is interesting to point out that the only other Ni-rich ataxite investigated here, Deep Spring, contains rare gas of "normal" cosmogenic composition and in much larger concentrations. Thus, it is tempting to attribute the anomalous rare gas in Washington County to diffusion which took place since the meteorite entered the earth's atmosphere. On the other hand, the anomalous rare gas could be of primordial origin. Neither origin, however, accounts for the big variations in concentrations between samples.

F.   The North Chilean Group

Four of the North Chilean meteorites (Leonard and De Violini, 1956) were included in this study in order to investigate the possibility of their belonging to a common fall. The problem was pointed out to us by Dr. C. A. Bauer, who also supplied three of the four samples employed. Due to the low concentrations of the cosmogenic rare gases in these samples, the relative errors in these measurements may be somewhat higher than the 5 percent found for most other measurements; unfortunately, the samples available were so small that only a single analysis was possible and therefore, no check of reproducibility could be made. With this reservation, it seems possible that Tocopilla, Coya Norte, and Rio Loa belong to the same fall. Negrillos, however, appears to belong to a different fall. It should be mentioned that by nature of the interpretation two meteorites could by coincidence appear to belong to the same fall. The converse does not appear possible.

ACKNOWLEDGMENTS

This work was supported by the joint program of the Office of Naval Research and the U.S. Atomic Energy Commission. The authors are indebted to all those whose generous cooperation, in making samples available, made this study possible. Special thanks are due R. B. Thorness and the staff of the shop which constructed the apparatus used in this research. The assistance of W. Brumm, J. R. Dickey, D. Maund and R. Oakes in making the measurements and computations is gratefully acknowledged.

REFERENCES

Bauer, C. A. 1961. Private communication.

Ebert, K. H., and H. Wanke. 1957. Ueber die Einwirkung der Hohenstrahlung auf Eisenmeteorite, Z. Naturforsch, 12a, 766-773.

Fechtig, H., W. Gentner, and G. Kistner. 1960. Raumliche Verteilung der Edelgasisotope im Eisenmeteoriten Treysa, Geochim. et Cosmochim. Acta, 18, 72-80.

Fireman, E. L. 1958. Distribution of helium-3 in the Carbo meteorite, Nature, 181, 1725.

Fireman, E. L. 1959. The distribution of helium-3 in the Grant meteorite and a determination of the original mass, Planetary and Space Sci., 1, 66-70.

Fireman, E. L., and J. De Felice. 1960. Argon-39 and tritium in meteorites, Geochim. et Cosmochim. Acta, 18, 183-192.

Fireman, E. L., and J. Zahringer. 1957. Depth variation of tritium and argon-37 produced by high energy protons in iron, Phys. Rev., 107, 1695-1698.

Fisher, D. E. 1961a. Cosmic ray ages of the
    Treysa and Sikhote-Alin meteorites, Nature, 190,
    225-227.
Fisher, D. E. 1961b. Origin of stone and iron
    meteorites, Nature, 190, 244-245.
Fisher, D. E. 1961c. Space erosion of the Grant
    meteorite, J. Geophys. Res., 66, 1509-1511.
Fisher, D. E., and O. A. Schaeffer. 1960. Cos-
    mogenic nuclear reactions in iron meteorites,
    Geochim. et Cosmochim. Acta, 20, 5-14.
Geiss, J., H. Oeschger, and P Signer. 1960. Ra-
    diation ages of chondrites, Z. f. Naturforsch,
    15a, 1016-1017.
Gerling, E. K., and L. K. Levskii. 1958. Cos-
    mic radiation products in the Sikhote-Alin me-
    teorite (English translation), Doklady Akad.
    Nauk USSR, 123, 420.
Gfeller, Ch., W. Herr, F. G. Houtermans, and H.
    Oeschger. 1959. C136 in meteorites, Helv.
    Phys. Acta, 32, 277.
Goebel, K., and J. Zahringer. 1961. Erzeugung
    von Tritium und Edelgasisotopen bei Bestrah-
    lung von Fe und Cu mit Protonen von 25 Gev
    Energie, Z. Naturforsch, 16a, 231-236.
Heymann, D., and O. A. Schaeffer, Exposure ages
    of some iron meteorites, Program of the 42nd
    Annual Meeting of the American Geophysical
    Union, p. 20, 1961.
Hoffman, J. H., and A. O. Nier. 1958. Production
    of helium in iron meteorites by the action of
    cosmic rays, Phys. Rev., 112, 2112-2117.
Hoffman, J. H., and A. O. Nier. 1959. The cos-
    mogenic He3 and He4 distribution in the mete-
    orite Carbo, Geochim. et. Cosmochim. Acta, 17,
    32-36.
Hoffman, J. H., and A. O. Nier. 1960. Cosmic-
    ray-produced helium in the Keen Mountain and
    Casas Grandes Meteorites, J. Geophys. Res.,
    65, 1063-1068.
Honda, M., and J. R. Arnold. 1961. Radioactive
    species produced by cosmic rays in the Aroos
    meteorite, Geochim. et Cosmochim. Acta, 23,
    219-232.
Honda, M., J. P. Shedlovsky, and J. R. Arnold.
    1961. Radioactive species produced by cosmic

rays in iron meteorites, Geochim. et Cosmochim. Acta, 22, 133-154.

Leonard, F. C., and R. De Violini. 1956. A classificational catalog of the meteoritic falls of the world, University of California Press, Berkeley and Los Angeles.

Martin, G. R. 1953. The origin of meteoritic helium and the age of meteorites. Geochim. et Cosmochim. Acta, 3, 288-309.

Paneth, F. A., P. Reasbeck, and K. I. Mayne. 1952. Helium-3 content and age of meteorites, Geochim. et Cosmochim. Acta, 2, 300-303.

Schaeffer, O. A. 1961. Cosmic ray ages of iron meteorites, Problems Related to Interplanetary Matter, National Academy of Sciences, National Research Council, Washington, D. C., Publication 845, 22-27.

Schaeffer, O. A., and D. E. Fisher. 1960a. Cosmogenic noble gases in Washington County meteorite, Nature, 183, 660-661.

Schaeffer, O. A., and D. E. Fisher. 1960b. Exposure ages of iron meteorites, Nature, 186, 1040-1042.

Schaeffer, O. A., and J. Zahringer. 1959. High sensitivity mass spectrometric measurements of stable helium and argon isotopes by high energy protons in iron, Phys. Rev., 113, 674-678.

Schaeffer, O. A., and J. Zahringer. 1960. Helium, neon and argon isotopes in some iron meteorites, Geochim. et Cosmochim. Acta, 19, 94-99.

Signer, P., and A. O. Nier. 1960. The distribution of cosmic-ray-produced rare gases in iron meteorites, J. Geophys. Res., 65, 2947-2964.

Signer, P., and A. O. Nier. 1961. The distribution of rare gases in iron meteorites, Problems Related to Interplanetary Matter, National Academy of Sciences, National Research Council, Washington, D. C., Publication 845, 31-44.

Sprenkel, E. 1959. Ph.D. thesis, University of Rochester. 1959.

Urey, H. C. 1959. Primary and secondary objects, J. Geophys. Res., 64, 1721-1737.

Vinogradov, A. P., I. K. Zadorozhnyi, and K. P. Florenskii. 1957. Content of the inert gases

in the Sikhote-Alin iron meteorite (English
translation), Geokhimiya, 6, 443-448.
Wanke, H. 1960a. Exposure ages for iron meteorites, Nature, 188, 1101-1102.
Wanke, H. 1960b. Sc45 als Reaktionsprodukte der
Hohenstrahlung in Meteoriten, II, Z. Naturforsch,
15a, 953-964.

PARMATMA S. GOEL

Carnegie Institute of Technology and
Tata Institute of Fundamental Research

Calculation of Production Rates

of Specific Nuclides

in Iron Meteoroids*

In two earlier publications of this series
(Ehmann and Kohman, 1958a and 1958b) some experimental work on cosmic-ray-induced Al^{26} and
Be^{10} in meteorites was described. Since then
the following additional cosmic-ray-produced
nuclides in meteorites have been discovered:
Ar^{39}(Fireman, 1958), Sc^{45} (Wanke, 1958), K^{40}
(Voshage and Hintenberger, 1959; Honda, 1959),
Cl^{36}(Sprenkel, 1959; Sprenkel et al., 1959; Gfeller et al., Honda et al., 1961), Mn^{53} (Shedlovsky,
1960; Honda et al., 1961) and Ar^{37}(Fireman and
DeFelice, 1960b; Stoenner et al., 1960). At present several groups of workers are actively engaged in making measurements of many short-lived
radionuclides in three freshly fallen meteorites;
Hamlet (chondrite), Aroos (siderite), and Bruder-
heim (chondrite) (Turkevich and Reed, 1960;
Arnold and Honda, 1960). The significance of the
study of cosmic-ray effects on meteorites has
been discussed previously (Geiss, 1959; Kohman
and Ehmann, 1958).

If one attempts to correlate the accumulated
data on cosmic-ray-produced nuclides in meteorites and to make some applications, one is faced
with the following questions: What are the absolute production rates of specific nuclides in
meteoroids? How do the production rates vary
with depth in a meteoroid? How do these rates

*Cosmic-Ray Induced Radioactivities in Meteor-
ites - III   This work has been supported by the
U.S. Atomic Energy Commission.

depend upon the size of the meteoroid? This paper is primarily devoted to answering these questions. The results of the calculations of the
production rates of specific nuclides in iron
meteoroids are given and their applications to
some problems in meteoritics as well as in cosmic
radiation are discussed.

RELATIVE STAR-PRODUCTION RATES IN IRON ALONG THE
BEAM

In this section we explore the experimental
data that will be used to construct a curve giving star-production rates by a beam of particles
having the same composition and spectrum as the
observed cosmic rays, incident normally upon a
plane infinite slab of iron, as a function of
depth below its surface.

a)   For Depths Between 20 and 100 cm
Recently Hoffman and Nier (1958) have measured
He^3 in a slice of Grant meteorite (pre-atmospheric radius about 40 cm) at various depths. The
He^3 distribution in this meteorite shows that
for depths between 20 and 80 cm from the surface
of a plane slab of iron meteorite exposed to a
normally incident beam of cosmic radiation the
star production decreases exponentially with a
mean free path of about 25 cm. We have taken
this value to hold generally for this depth
range.

b)   For Depths Between 10 and 20 cm
The cross sections for the production of H^3
and Ar^{37} by 6.2-and 1.0-Gev protons and for H^3
by 3.0-Gev protons in thick iron targets, as a
function of depth, have been measured by Fireman
and Zahringer (1957). According to their data
the H^3-production rate is approximately proportional to the Ar^{37}-production rate at high energies and can therefore be taken as a measure of
star-production rate. By exposing thick brass
targets sandwiched with steel foils to a 440-
Mev external proton beam of the Carnegie synchrocyclotron, and measuring the gross beta activity
in the steel foils as a function of intervening
brass thickness (details in Appendix I), we can
approximate the depth dependence of the star-

production rates in a thick iron target at this
energy.

Figure 1 gives the relative star-production

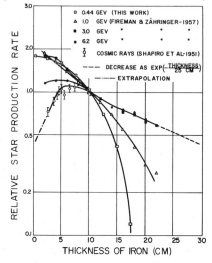

Figure 1. Relative star-production rates
along beams of protons of different energies in thick iron targets, as a function
of the intervening thickness. The curve
for each energy is normalized to unity at
10 cm thickness.

rates as a function of depth, normalized to unity at 10 cm depth for protons of 6.2, 3.0, 1.0
and 0.44 Gev. It is noted that the slopes of
the curves at 6.2 and 3.0 Gev are practically
the same for thicknesses greater than 10 cm. At
20 cm their slopes correspond closely to an absorption mean free path of 25 cm, the value mentioned earlier for greater thicknesses. Since
lower-energy primary particles should be relatively ineffective beyond 10 cm, we take the
mean of the variation of star-production rate
versus depth at 3.0- and 6.2-Gev proton bombardment as representative of cosmic-ray star production for depths between 10 and 20 cm.
c) For Depths Between 0 and 10 cm
   Shapiro et al. (1951) have measured directly

the star-production rates in nuclear emulsions
exposed to cosmic radiation in the stratosphere
(13 g cm^{-2}) at a latitude of 56° N under various
thicknesses of lead absorbers arranged in spherical geometry. Their data extrapolated to free
space and corrected for the difference in the
geometrical cross section for iron and lead are
shown in Figure 1. At 56° N, the geomagnetic
cut-off for the primary protons is 0.95 Gev, so
we have complete information on the relative star-
production rates up to 100 cm depth for primary
particles of energies greater than 0.95 Gev.
For low energy primaries, we use the production
rates corresponding to 440-Mev. protons.

ABSOLUTE STAR-PRODUCTION RATES IN IRON AND STONE
METEOROIDS

To obtain absolute star-production rates one
needs to know (a) the cosmic-ray energy spectrum
in interplanetary space and (b) the total star-
production cross section in iron as a function
of energy.

a) The Primary Cosmic-Ray Flux

Singer (1958) has summarized the values of the
flux of primary cosmic radiation at different
latitudes in a recent review articles. At 56°
N the primary particle flux is 0.22 particle cm^{-2}
sec^{-1} sterad^{-1}. This covers protons of energy
greater than 0.95 Gev and alpha particles of
energy greater than 1.2 Gev. The flux at lower
energy is not very well determined because of
the uncertainty in the low-energy cut-off. It
is certain that in the period of minimum solar
activity primary particles do exist with energies
down to 100 Mev (Neher, 1956). The increase in
ionization between 56° N to 61° N indicates that
the low-energy primary flux can be taken equivalent to 0.10 proton cm^{-2} sec^{-1} sterad^{-1} of 0.4
Gev average energy (Neher, 1958).

b) Star Production Cross Section in Iron

The inelastic cross section in iron has been
found to be fairly constant between 1 and 50 Gev,
and can be taken as 610 mb (Brenner and Williams,

1957). Measurements at lower energies generally give higher values for cross sections. At 650-Mev proton energy, the inelastic cross section in copper is found to be 850 ± 50 mb (Moskalev and Gavrilovskii, 1957). Taking the cross sections as proportional to $A^{2/3}$ gives 780 mb for the inelastic cross section of iron at this energy; this value is used as the cross section for all of the primaries below 0.95 Gev. Since not all of the interactions yield stars*, the above values have to be reduced somewhat to get the star-production cross section. From the star-size distribution pattern discussed in the next section, we find that about 24% of the total interactions are of the type in which only neutral secondaries are emitted. Thus values of (0.76) (610 mb) = 464 mb and (0.76) (780 mb) = 593 mb have been taken for the star-production cross sections in iron meteorites for the high- and low-energy primaries respectively.

c) Star-Production Rate Along the Beam in Iron

The absolute star-production rate at the surface of a plane infinite iron slab exposed to a normally incident beam of cosmic radiation is given by:

$$\frac{F_1 \times \sigma_1 \times N}{\alpha_{Fe}} + \frac{F_2 \times \sigma_2 \times N}{\alpha_{Fe}} \quad \text{star sec}^{-1}\text{g}^{-1}\text{sterad}^{-1}$$

Where F_1 = flux of high-energy primaries = 0.22 particle $\text{cm}^{-2}\text{sec}^{-1}\text{sterad}^{-1}$

F_2 = flux of low-energy primaries = 0.10 particle $\text{cm}^{-2}\,\text{sec}^{-1}\text{sterad}^{-1}$

σ_1 = star-production cross section at high energies = 464 mb

σ_2 = star-production cross section at low energies = 593 mb

---

* a "star" is defined here as a nuclear reaction in which at least one charged secondary, or prong, is emitted, the emergent primary not being counted.

N = Avogadro's number = 6.02×10^{23} atoms mol^{-1}

α_{Fe} = atomic weight of iron = 56 g mol^{-1}

Using the above relation to calculate the absolute star-production rate at the surface, and the depth dependence derived in Section I, the absolute star-production rate as a function of distance along the beam in the metal can be calculated. The results are plotted in Figure 2.

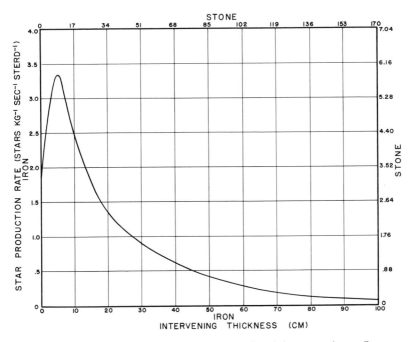

Figure 2. Absolute star-production rate along the beam, as a function of thickness of intervening material. The ordinates give the number of stars produced per kilogram of material per second under irradiation from unit solid angle by cosmic radiation of present-day quality and intensity.

d) <u>Absolute Star-Production Rates in Iron Meteoroids</u>

Assuming that the lateral shower spread is

small, the results of Figure 2 can be integrated over all directions for an isotropic flux striking a solid iron body. This has been done by numerical integration for spherical meteoroids of radii 5, 10, 20, 30, 40 and 50 cm and also for very large meteoroid ($\underline{R} = \infty$). The results are presented in Figure 3.

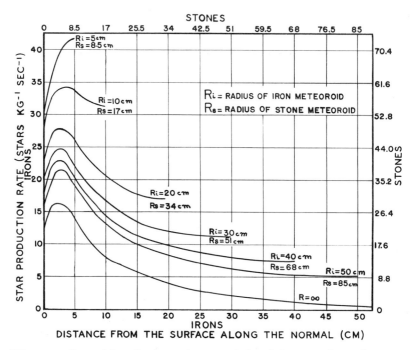

Figure 3. Absolute star-production rates in spherical meteoroids of different radii, as a function of the distance from the surface measured along the normal.

e)   Absolute Star-Production Rates in Stone Meteoroids

The average chemical composition of stone meteorites is: O 40.4%, Si 21%, Mg 16.2%, Fe 15% Al 1.7%, S 2.2%, Ca 1.8%, and some other elements in smaller concentrations (Levin et al., 1956). Using the well known fact that at high energies the star-production cross section in various elements is proportional to the geometrical cross section, $\pi r_c^2 A^{2/3}$ (Atkinson et al., 1959), we can calculate the star-production rate in stone meteoroids. Taking the density of stone meteoroids as 3.60 g cm^{-3} (Urey, 1959) and that of iron as 7.9 g cm^{-3}, we find that a thickness of 1.70 cm of the stone meteoroid is equivalent to a thickness of 1.00 cm of iron in attenuating the cosmic-ray star production by the same factor, and that the specific star-production rate in stone is about 1.76 times the corresponding value for iron. Therefore, by multiplying the abscissa and the ordinates of Figure 2 (corresponding to iron targets) by 1.70 and 1.76 respectively, we obtain the corresponding curve for stones. Similarly the curves of Figure 3, apply, with the different scales indicated, to the star-production rates in stone meteoroids of radii 8.5, 17, 34, 51, 68, and 85 cm and also for a very large meteoroid ($R = \infty$).

PRODUCTION OF INDIVIDUAL NUCLIDES IN IRON METEOROIDS

In the present work we make a simplifying assumption that the whole meteoroid mass is composed of Fe^{56}. The relatively smaller contributions from Fe^{54} and nickel isotopes should not be so different from those from Fe^{56} as to affect the results except for the products which are very near to iron and nickel--e.g., Mn^{53}, Mn^{54}, Ni^{59}, Fe^{60}, Co^{60} and Ni^{63}. Among these heavy products only Mn^{53} and Mn^{54} are treated in the present paper; their production rates accordingly have larger uncertainty than those of other nuclides. In specimens containing gross inclusions of troilite (sulfide), schreibersite (phosphide), and graphite (carbon) there will be differences, but mainly in the lighter products which are not considered here.

a) Production-Rate Distribution Among Elements

Recently Lal et al. (1958) have calculated the cosmic-ray production rates of some radionuclides in the atmosphere from the characteristics of cosmic-ray stars. In this paper a similar approach has been adopted.

Table 1. Relative abundance of various particles in the secondaries of stars

Author(s)	Experiment			He^3/He^4	He^3/H^3	$\frac{s}{1}$
	Projectile	Target	Technique			
Martin et al. (1954)	340-Mev protons	Steel	H^3 by counting, He3/He4 by mass spectrometer	0.048	0.615	-
Bailey (1956)	190-Mev protons	Nickel	Magnetic analyzer	0.105	0.95	0.87
Ostroumev (1957)	130-Mev protons 460-Mev protons 660-Mev protons	Ag and Br Ag and Br Ag and Br	Nuclear emulsion	- - -	- - -	0.81 0.855 0.80
Schaeffer and Zahringer (1958)	0.16-Gev protons 0.43-Gev protons 3.0-Gev protons	Iron Iron Iron	Mass spectrometer	0.09 0.10 0.18	- - -	- - -
Bieri (1958)	6.2-Gev protons	Copper	Mass spectrometer	0.171	-	-

Let s and d be the fractions of singly- and doubly-charged secondary particles emitted in the stars produced in iron meteoroids. Since in the secondaries the abundance of particles with charge greater than two is very low, the sum $(s + d)$ can be taken equal to unity. Let the fraction of stars having t prongs be n_t. The average fractional yield of various elements will be given as follows:

$$f(\text{Mn}) = n_1 s \text{ atoms per star.}$$

$$f(\text{Cr}) = n_2 s^2 + n_1 d \text{ atoms per star.}$$

$$f(\text{V}) = n_3 s^3 + 2n_2 sd \text{ atoms per star.}$$

$$f(\text{Ti}) = n_4 s^4 + 3n_3 s^2 d + n_2 d^2 \text{ atoms per star.}$$

$$f(\text{Sc}) = n_5 s^5 + 4n_4 s^3 d + 3n_3 sd^2 \text{ atoms per star.}$$

Similar expressions can be written for the formation of other elements.

n_t can be obtained from the knowledge of the star-size distribution in nuclear emulsions. The integral of the distribution can be represented by an expression of the form $N_t = e^{-\beta t}$, where N_t is the fraction of stars with more than t prongs. n_t is simply $N_{t-1} - N_t$. The value of β for stars in silver and bromine at an atmospheric depth of 13 g cm^{-2} (altitude of 29 km), is 0.198 ± 0.016 and is found to remain constant within measurement uncertainty under lead absorbers of thickness up to 15 cm (170 g cm^{-2}) (Birnbaum et al., 1952). At mountain altitude (3.5 km, 675 g cm^{-2}) β is somewhat different, having a value of 0.33. However, here again, it does not change under lead absorbers of thickness up to 28 cm (320 g cm^{-2}) (George and Jason, 1949). This large change from 0.198 to 0.33 reflects the fact that at greater depths the low-energy stars are in preponderance. It is reasonable to assume that, in a meteoroid, in the first two or three interaction lengths the star-size distribution pattern remains practically unchanged. Since in the present calculations iron meteoroids of radius up to only 50 cm ($\sim$400 g cm^{-2}) are considered, it is

reasonable to treat β as constant at all depths.
Star produced by π-mesons, which will play a
significant role at large depths, will not fit
in this pattern. Until some experiments on thick
iron targets sandwiched with emulsions and exposed to high-energy protons are done, it does not
appear feasible to estimate quantitatively how
these variations will affect the present calculations.

After the work of Barbour (1954) on cosmic ray
stars in iron foils, β will be taken as 0.28 for
stars in iron targets. To obtain s (and d) we
refer to Table 1, where some data from the literature on the abundance of various secondaries in
high energy reactions have been surveyed. A
reasonable choice is s = 0.83 and d = 0.17. The
production of most elements (except hydrogen and
helium) is not very sensitive to small variations
in s.

The yields of various elements from nuclear reactions in iron have been calculated and presented in Figure 4.

Yield Distribution Among Isotopes (Z = 17-25)

We now want to find out how the yield per star
for an element is partitioned among its various
isotopes. These distributions have been estimated using Rudstam's (1955) empirical formula
for the spallation yields with high-energy protons according to which the relative production
rates (cross section, σ) of various isotopes of
atomic number Z can be calculated from the relation:

$$\ln \sigma(Z,A) \propto PA - R(Z - SA)^2$$

where P, R, and S are adjustable parameters. The
following set of values has been taken for these
parameters: P = 0.215, R = 1.48, and S = 0.467.
The values of R and S, which are not very dependent on the energy of the projectile, are the
average from about 20 different bombardments on
various medium-weight elements (Rudstam, 1956).
The parameter P is energy-dependent, and the
above value corresponds to the proton energy of
about 400 Mev. This choice is reasonable because
the most of the nuclides are produced in stars

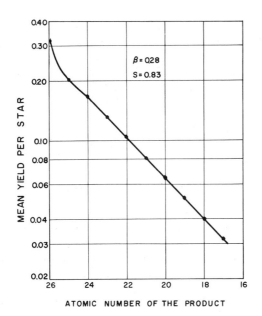

Figure 4. Mean production frequency of various elements per star due to cosmic-ray-induced nuclear reactions in iron.

that are caused by the secondaries with energies of this order of magnitude.

The production rates per star of most nuclides down to Cl^{34} have been calculated and are listed in Table 2. Nuclides whose production rate is less than 0.00005 per star are not entered in the table.

Tritium and Helium Production Rates

In 190-Mev proton bombardment of nickel the fraction of tritium in singly-charged secondaries is 0.0147 (Bailey, 1956). This figure can be taken only for the cosmic-ray stars that have an excitation energy less than 190 Mev and consequently have less than about four prongs (Camerini et al., 1951). Of the secondaries from larger stars 17% are doubly charged particles, 36% are "grey" particles (protons of 25-500 Mev, π mesons of less than 8 Mev, and tritons of greater than

75 Mev) and the remaining 47% are singly-charged particles of low energy (Camerini et al.,
1951). From the data of the Bristol group
(Daniel, 1957), the abundance of tritium in
"grey" particles is 0.07. The range of these
tritons in iron will mostly lie between about
0.5 cm (energy ~80 Mev) and 10 cm (energy ~450
Mev). Their energy distribution is such (Daniel,
1957) that most of them will travel an average
distance of about 2 cm (energy ~175 Mev) in iron
before coming to rest by ionization loss. Some
of them will disappear because they will under-
go nuclear reactions rather than stop. Cross
sections for complex projectiles are larger than
for protons, and the mean free path for nuclear
reactions for tritons and deutrons together, in
nuclear emulsion is only about half of the mean
free path calculated from the geometrical cross
section (Camerini et al., 1950). The same is
also true for high-energy alpha particles (Appa
Rao et al., 1956). The mean free path of tritons in iron is so calculated to be 6 cm. The
fraction of tritons in "grey" tracks escaping
nuclear reactions will thus be exp (-2 cm/6 cm)
= 0.72.

The average number of secondaries per star is:

$$\underline{f}(\underline{s} + \underline{d}) = \sum_{\underline{t}=\underline{1}} \underline{t}n_{\underline{t}} = \sum_{\underline{t}=\underline{1}} \underline{t} \left[\exp(-\beta \underline{t} + \beta) - \exp(-\beta \underline{t}) \right]$$

$$= \frac{1}{1-\exp(-\beta)} = 4.10 \text{ prongs per star.}$$

The number of secondaries from high-energy stars
(those with more than three prongs) is, $\underline{f}(\underline{s} + \underline{d})$
= 4.10 - 0.244 - 2(0.185) - 3(0.140) = 3.065
prongs per (total) star. The tritium accumulation due to "grey" tracks is thus (3.065)(0.36)
(0.07)(0.72) = 0.0556 tritons per star. The low-
energy secondaries from high-energy stars con-
tribute (3.07)(0.47)(0.0147) = 0.0212 tritons
per star. Finally from stars with up to three
prongs the tritium production is (4.10 - 3.065)
(0.83)(0.0147) = 0.0126 tritons per star. Therefore, the total H^3 accumulation is 0.0556 +
0.0212 + 0.0126 = 0.0894 tritons per star.

The fraction of He^3 in doubly-charged secondar-

Table 2. Independent yield per star of various nuclides in spallation of iron by cosmic radiation*

A \ Z	25 Mn	24 Cr	23 V	22 Ti	21 Sc	20 Ca	19 K	18 Ar	17 Cl
54	.06547	.00102							
53	.05170	.03209	.00098						
52	.02140	.05254	.00640						
51	.00466	.04575	.02219	.00061					
50	.00053	.02078	.03999	.00405					
49		.00495	.03803	.01528					
48		.00062	.01889	.03028	.00253				
47			.00492	.03137	.01042	.00018			
46			.00068	.01708	.02259	.00154			
45				.00467	.02570	.00699	.00010		
44				.00073	.01535	.01625	.00094		
43					.00461	.02070	.00464		
42					.00080	.01349	.01209	.00056	
41					.00007	.00460	.01648	.00314	
40						.00083	.01176	.00868	.00033
39						.00006	.00443	.01295	.00196
38							.00087	.01017	.00612
37							.00009	.00418	.01003
36								.00090	.00860
35								.00010	.00394
34									.00092
Sum for element	0.202	0.169	0.132	0.105	0.820	0.0650	0.0514	0.0407	0.0320

* Stable nuclides are printed in bold face.

Table 3.   Total yields per star in iron, and absolute production rates at the center of a spherical iron meteoroid of 10 cm radius, of some nuclides

Nuclide	Half-life	Modes of production considered	Production frequency (atoms star^{-1})	Absolute production rate (atoms sec^{-1}kg^{-1})
Sc^{45}	Stable	Sc^{45},Ca^{45},Ti^{45}	0.0373	1.17
K^{41}	Stable	K^{41},Ca^{41},Sc^{41}	0.0243	0.76
K^{39}	Stable	$K^{39},Cl^{39},Ar^{39},Ca^{39}$	0.0194	0.61
Ar^{40}	Stable	Ar^{40},Cl^{40}	0.0090	0.28
Ar^{40}	Stable	$Ar^{40},Cl^{40},11\% K^{40}$	0.0103	0.32
Ar^{38}	Stable	Ar^{38},Cl^{38},K^{38}	0.0172	0.54
Ar^{36}	Stable	Ar^{36},Cl^{36}	0.0095	0.30
He^{4}	Stable	He^{4}	0.609	19.1
He^{3}	Stable	He^{3},H^{3}	0.1750	5.49
Mn^{54}	320 d	Mn^{54}	0.0655	2.06
Mn^{53}	2×10^{6} y	Mn^{53},Fe^{53}	0.0982	3.08
Cr^{51}	28 d	Cr^{51},Mn^{51}	0.0504	1.58
V^{49}	330 d	V^{49},Cr^{49}	0.0430	1.35
Ti^{44}	10^{3} y	Ti^{44}	0.00073	0.023
Sc^{46}	85 d	Sc^{46}	0.0226	0.71
Ca^{45}	164 d	Ca^{45}	0.0070	0.22
Ca^{41}	1.1×10^{5} y	Ca^{41},Sc^{41}	0.0047	0.15
K^{40}	1.31×10^{9} y	K^{40}	0.0118	0.37
Ar^{42}	10 y	Ar^{42}	0.00056	0.018
Ar^{39}	325 y	Ar^{39},Cl^{39}	0.0149	0.47
Ar^{37}	37 d	Ar^{37}	0.0042	0.13
Cl^{36}	3.08×10^{5} y	Cl^{36}	0.0086	0.27
H^{3}	12.5 y	H^{3}	0.0894	2.81

ies is taken as $He^3/(He^3 + He^4) = 0.123$, which is the average of the results of 0.43- and 3.0-Gev proton bombardment on iron (Schaeffer and Zahringer, 1958) (see Table 1). This gives a He^3-production rate of $(4.10)(0.17)(0.123) = 0.0856$ atoms per star. Since H^3 also decays into He^3, the total He^3 accumulation is 0.175 atoms per star.

Total and Absolute Production Rates

The previously described calculations give the independent yields only of the various nuclides considered, before changes due to radioactive decay. The total yield of many nuclides is significantly greater because of the indirect formation through precursors. In practically all cases the lifetimes of the precursors are short enough so that the total rather than the independent yield is of most interest.

Table 3 gives the total production frequencies (atoms per star) of a number of nuclides which are of interest in studies of iron meteorites. In the case of Ar^{40}, two figures are given, without and with the contribution from K^{40} decay; the actual yield in all cases will be intermediate.

Production of Fe^{53}, which decays into Mn^{53}, takes place in interactions in which only neutral secondaries are emitted. By extrapolation such "neutral-prong-stars" are calculated as 0.323 per star (visible "star" defined earlier). Making a crude assumption that the neutron emission in these "neutral-prong-stars" were to follow a prong-distribution pattern with $\beta = 0.28$, as for charged prongs, the production frequency of Fe^{53} from iron target of normal isotopic composition would be 0.323 $(0.0584)(0.244) + (0.9168)(0.140) + (0.0219)(0.104) + (0.0031)(0.08) = 0.323$
$0.01427 + 0.12820 + 0.00228 + 0.00025 = .0465$
per star. Actual distribution in neutron emission is likely to be steeper ($\beta > 0.28$), but the isotopic composition of iron is such that the above result is not very sensitive to the value of

Table 3 also gives the absolute (total) specific production rates of the same nuclides in a

typical case: at the center of spherical iron
meteoroid of 10 cm radius. These figures were
obtained with the help of Figure 2, which can be
used to make similar calculations for other cases.

Limitations of the Present Approach

Unfortunately in our present discussion we
have to exclude some nuclides whose study in
iron meteorites is quite important. The production of the light nuclides like Be^{10} and C^{14} cannot be estimated in the above way because they
invoke a different mechanism for their formation.
They are mainly ejected as large aggregates of
nucleons (fragmentation), and the present approach
of prong analysis does not apply. Also we have
omitted the calculations for the production of
nuclides like Al^{26} and Ne isotopes because the
stars involved in their formation have 10 to 15
prongs. When the excitation energy is so high,
there are frequently emitted particles of charge
greater than two; such stars do not fit in the
size-distribution pattern outlined above.

COMPARISON OF CALCULATIONS WITH EXPERIMENTAL DATA

Depth Independence of Production-Rate Ratios

In Section II it was stated that the experiments
of George and Jason (1949) and Birnbaum et al.
(1952) show that the size-distribution pattern
of cosmic-ray stars does not change significantly
under various thicknesses of lead absorbers.
This is true for stars produced in silver and
bromine nuclei as well as in the carbon, nitrogen, and oxygen nuclei of emulsions. One might
expect, then, that the star-size distribution
pattern should be essentially the same throughout a meteoroid, either iron or stone, whose
radius is no greater than about three interaction lengths (R < 70 cm for irons, R ≤ 120 cm
for stones). This means that when the product
levels are high enough to be easily measured,
implying that the meteoroid was small or the
specimen was near the surface, the ratio of the
production rates of any two nuclides should be
practically independent of the shape and size of
the meteoroid. In a large meteoroid at great
depths the low-energy stars will be relatively

more frequent, and here the relative yields also
are likely to change with depth.

The observed constancy (or smallness of the
variations) in most values of He^3/He^4, He^3/Ar^{38},
He^3/Ne^{20}, etc. from different iron meteorites
whose sizes are not very large (Gentner and Zahringer, 1957; Ebert and Wanke, 1958) supports
our conclusion.

Stone meteorites show a variable chemical composition, and inhomogeneties may occur even in
the same meteorite. Since the relative formation
rates of different nuclies from different target elements will be different, the ratios of any
two nuclides in different samples may, in general,
not be the same. An indication that the ratios
may be the same in objects of the same composition is given by certain data, presented in Table
4. Here the meteorites are grouped such that
the ratios Ne^{20}/Ne^{22} are the same for the meteorites of each group. This perhaps implies that
the abundance of the target elements responsible
for the gross production of neon isotopes is the
same in the meteorites belonging to one particular group. In the last column we give the $He^3/$
Ne^{22} ratios. It is evident that for the meteorites falling in one group these ratios are nearly the same, with one exception. A similar comparison of Ar^{36}/Ar^{38} and He^3/Ar^{38} fails to show
similar trends, but this does not disprove the
suggested generalization.

If the implication in the above grouping could
be confirmed by chemical analyses of the meteorites, it would lend definite support to our earlier conclusion that in all meteoroids which are
not very large the relative production rates of
any two nuclides should be independent of the
depth of the sample material. Such a generalization would be very useful. For example, simulta-
neous measurements of several radionuclides in a
sample of a meteorite, in conjunction with the
present calculations, could give directly information about the mean cosmic-ray intensity in
past time periods comparable to the mean lifetimes of the radionuclides.

Table 4.   Comparison of He^3/Ne^{22} and Ne^{20}/Ne^{22}

Meteorite[a]	Ne^{20}/Ne^{22}	Ar^{38} $(10^{-8}cm^3g^{-1})$	Ne^{22} $(10^{-8}cm^3g^{-1})$	He^3 $(10^{-8}cm^3g^{-1})$	He^3/Ne^{22}
Elenovka	1.0	0.42	5.3	30	5.7
Saratov	1.0	0.62	5	30	6.0
Zhovtnevyi Khutor	0.83	0.76	7.5	40	5.3
Bjurbole	2.0	0.18	1.7	15	8.8
Pervomaiskii Poselok grey variety	2.1	0.20	0.8	6	7.5
Kunashak grey variety	1.8	0.10	0.42	4	9.5
Okhansk	1.7	0.21	0.6	15	25

(a) Gerling and Levskii (1956)

Table 5. Comparison of calculated and experimental values of nuclide ratios in iron meteorites

Nuclide Ratio	Calculated value	Observed value	Author(s)
He^3/He^4	0.29	0.25 - 0.32	Ebert and Wanke (1957)
Ar^{38}/Ar^{36}	1.8*	1.7	Gentner and Zahringer (1957)
He^3/Ar^{38}	10.2	15	Gentner and Zahringer (1957)
He/Sc^{45}	21.0	23	Wanke (1958)
Sc^{45}/Ar^{36}	3.94*	5	Wanke (1958)

*The Ar^{36} production rates refer to only those from the spallation of iron. The possible production by the reaction $Cl^{35}(n,\gamma)Cl^{36}(\beta^-)Ar^{36}$ in lawrencite inclusions in the meteorite has not been taken into account; if important, it would cause the observed ratio to be lower than the calculated.

Production-Rate Ratios of Stable Nuclides in Iron Meteorites

Measurements on the ratios of various cosmic-ray-produced stable nuclides in iron meteorites have been made by several workers. In Table 5 the calculated values for some of these ratios are compared with the existing measurements. As can be seen, the agreement is very good.

Production-Rate Ratios of Radionuclides in Iron Meteorites

In Table 6 are compared the calculated ratios of the production rates of some pairs of radionuclides with the corresponding measured saturation activity ratios. The two sets of values do not show as good an agreement as noted earlier for stable nuclide pairs. However, because of the uncertainties both in the calculations and the experimental measurements of radionuclides (experimental determinations of stable nuclides, excluding Sc^{45}, have good accuracy) we do not believe that the disagreements can be taken to indicate variations of cosmic-ray intensity in past times.

The poor agreement for the Mn^{53}/Cl^{36} ratio can be attributed to the under-estimation of Mn^{53}-production rate. In nuclear emulsion work the fraction of one-prong stars, which are responsible for the production of Mn^{53}, is obtained only by extrapolation of the star-size distribution curve. It is quite likely that this extrapolation is not valid and that one-prong stars are much more frequent than expected.

The agreement between the calculated and observed ratios is satisfactory for the case Cl^{36}/Ar^{39} and surprisingly good in the case Ar^{39}/H^3.

In comparing the calculated ratio Ar^{39}/Ar^{37} we prefer the laboratory production ratio in iron to the meteoritic ratio since the latter suffers from two uncertainties: (a) large error in Ar^{37} measurement in Aroos meteorite because the measurements were made three months after the fall (Fireman and DeFelice, 1960b); (b) possible variation in cosmic-ray intensity. Poor agreement between the calculated Ar^{39}/Ar^{37} ratio and

Table 6. Comparison of calculated and experimental values of radionuclide ratios in iron meteorites

Nuclide ratio	Calculated value	Observed value	Meteorite	Reference to observed value
Mn^{53}/Cl^{36}	11.4	43.6	Odessa	Honda et al.(1961)
Cl^{36}/Ar^{39}	0.58	0.98	Sikhote Alin	Sprenkel et al. (1959)
Ar^{39}/H^{3}	0.167	0.167	Treysa	Fireman and DeFelice (1960a)
Ar^{39}/Ar^{37}	3.55	0.71	Aroos	Fireman and DeFelice (1960b)
		1.24*	Iron target	Schaeffer and Zahringer (1959)

* Laboratory production in iron by 0.43 Gev protons

the bombardment results seems to be due to the uncertainties in the calculations.

Uncertainties in the Calculations

Summarizing the discussions of the last two sub-sections, we note that the calculated ratios of the production rates of 9 pairs of nuclides (of which 8 are independent pairs) are in good agreement with the experimental observations except for two cases; $Mn53/Cl36$ and $Ar39/Ar37$. A likely explanation for the case $Mn53/Cl36$ has also been given. We believe that, except for products very near the target elements, the present calculations predict production rates with an accuracy of a factor of 1.5 (standard deviation basis).

It has been pointed out (Honda and Lal, 1960) that Rudstam's empirical formula with the values of parameters chosen in the present work, although predicting satisfactory cross sections for the production of a large number of nuclides, occasionally gives values which are in serious error, particularly for products close to stability line. A different set of parameters ($P = 10.2E^{0.63}$, $S = 0.472$, $R = 1.9$, where E is the energy of incident protons in Mev) has been suggested to accommodate all cases (Honda and Lal, 1960). Using the alternate parameters, appropriate at 730 Mev, viz. $P = 0.16$, $S = 0.472$ and $R = 1.9$ in the approach of the present author, Shedlovsky (1960) has calculated yield of nuclides in iron meteoroids. In addition, for calculating $Mn53$-production rate, Shedlovsky, instead of using Rudstam's empirical relation, has used some interpolated data from high energy bombardment of copper and iron. In Table 7 we compare three sets of values of the ratios of various nuclide pairs; the experimental values, the values calculated in the present work, and the values calculated by Shedlovsky. The calculations with alternate parameters give a better value of $Ar39/Ar37$ ratio but do not seem to improve the overall picture greatly.

We would like to stress that neither calculations of the present type nor cross-section measurements on thin targets exposed to protons can give an entirely satisfactory picture of the

Table 7.   A comparison of the experimental results, the present calculations, and
the calculations of Shedlovsky

Nuclide pair	Observed ratio[*]	Calculated ratio	
		This work $P=.215, S=.467, \bar{R}=1.48$	Shedlovsky (1960)
Mn^{53}/Cl^{36}	43.6	11.4	6.26
Cl^{36}/Ar^{39}	0.98	0.58	0.92
Ar^{39}/H^3	0.167	0.167	0.160
Ar^{39}/Ar^{37}	0.71 1.24[**]	3.55	1.75
He^3/He^4	0.25-0.32	0.29	0.26
Ar^{38}/Ar^{36}	1.7	1.8	1.4
He^3/Ar^{38}	15	10.2	8.6
He/Sc^{45}	23	21.0	19.1
Sc^{45}/Ar^{36}	5	3.94	3.10

[*] For references see Tables 5 and 6.

[**] Laboratory production in iron by 0.43 Gev
protons.

nuclear reactions in meteoroids. It is expected
that in a meteoroid a large fraction of nuclear
reactions are induced by secondary particles, especially π-mesons (I am indebted to Professor
B. Peters for pointing out this to me.) and neutrons. (Secondary protons will be less important
because of their short range due to ionization.)
The pion-induced stars have a drastically different prong-distribution pattern from those produced by protons (Ivanova et al., 1960; Blau and
Oliver, 1956; Sprague et al., 1954), and even for
neutrons the yield pattern may differ from that
of protons. Experimental study of the depth-de-
pendence of nuclear reactions and specific products in laboratory bombardments at different
energies appears to be the best way of greatly
improving the basis for these calculations.

Acknowledgements

I take great pleasure in thanking Professor T.
P. Kohman for his interest and encouragement in
the completion of this work. His advice, suggestions, and critical comments have resulted in
many improvements. I thank Dr. J. P. Shedlovsky
for calling my attention to several errors in an
earlier version of this paper; Professor A. A.
Caretto, Jr., for helpful comments; Dr. R. R.
Daniel (Bombay) for making available the data of
the Bristol group on the analysis of "grey" tracks;
and Dr. D. L. Morrison for help in the experiment
described in Appendix I.
     The early part of this work was carried out at
the Tata Institute of Fundamental Research, Bombay, where I received many useful suggestions
from Professor B. Peters and Professor D. Lal,
to whom I would like to express my gratitude.
The financial support of the United States Atomic
Energy Commission for the work done at Carnegie
Institute of Technology is gratefully acknowledged.

APPENDIX I.

DEPTH DEPENDENCE OF REACTION RATES ALONG 440-MEV
PROTON BEAM

The relative star-production rates by 440-Mev
protons in a thick target, as a function of depth,
were determined experimentally using an external
proton beam of the Carnegie Tech Synchrocyclotron.
The protons, when fully accelerated, diffuse out
of the machine tangentially to the circumference
of the magnetic field. The 12-foot thick wall
of the cyclotron room has a hole in a direction
tangent to the field. The area of this "proton
window" is 2" x 2" at the end. Protons diffusing
out in the direction of the hole emerge from the
window as a well-collimated beam. To improve
the collimation further a set of lead bricks was
placed against the window, extending the 2" x 2"
hole by an additional 6 inches.
   The target consisted of eight stainless steel
foils each 0.009" thick and 2" x 2" in cross-
sectional area. These foils were alternated with
brass absorbers 2" x 2" in area and 1" thick.
The foils and absorbers were normal to and center-
ed on the beam axis. The irradiation lasted for
three hours.
   After the bombardment the foils were removed
and mounted for beta counting. Since the gross
activity should give a better measure of the total star-production rate than the activity of
any specific nuclear reaction product, no chemical separation was made. Each foil was covered
with a 1/4" thick brass disc having a 3/4" diameter hole at the center so that the activity
belonging to the central portion of the foil only
was detected. The counting was done with an end-
window Geiger counter, the foils being 0.7" from
the 1.1"-diameter window. The counting started
three hours after the end of irradiation. It
took less than a half hour to complete a set of
observations. In the beginning the activity in
the first foil gave 2300 ± 35 counts min^{-1}. The
apparent half-life of the gross activity was approximately two hours.

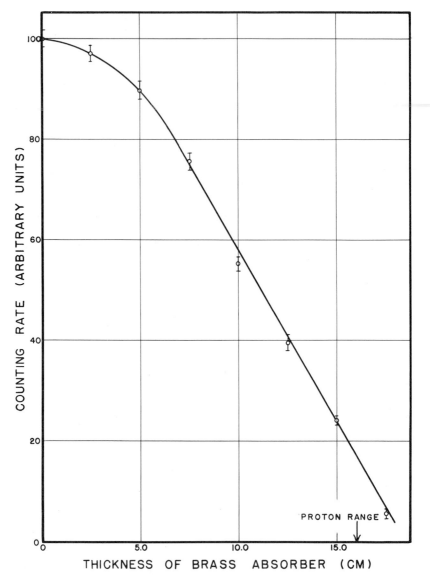

Figure 5. Measured relative radioactivity induced by 440-Mev protons in steel foils, as a
function of thickness of intervening brass absorbers.

A second set of observations were taken by
counting the foils without any coverings so that
the counter was exposed to the whole foil. It
was expected that this would reflect the effect
of the lateral spread of the beam. The results
of this set of measurements also showed the same
depth dependence as in the earlier cases, indicating that the lateral spread does not cause
significant error.

The results on the relative counting rates
(which would be the relative star-production
rates) as a function of intervening brass thickness are shown in Figure 5.

Since the star production in most meteoroids
by low-energy primaries constitutes only a small
fraction of the total star production (except
very near the surface) any small errors in the
present data should not give appreciable errors
in the total star-production rates in most meteoroids as calculated in the section on absolute
star-production rates in iron and stone meteoroids.

REFERENCES

Appa Rao, M.V.K., Daniel, R. R. and Neelakantan,
    K. A. (1956) Nuclear disintegrations produced
    in nuclear emulsions by α-particles of great
    energy. Proc. Ind. Acad. Sci. 43A, 181.
Arnold, J. R. and Honda, M. (1960) Private com-
    munication.
Atkinson, J. H., Hess, W. N., Perez-Mendez, V.
    and Wallace, R. W. (1959) Neutron cross section
    measurements at 4.5 Bev. Phys. Rev. Letters 2,
    168.
Bailey, L. E. (1956) Angle and energy distribu-
    tions of charged particles from the high-energy
    nuclear bombardment of various elements.(Thesis),
    UCRL-3334.
Barbour, I. G.(1954) Emulsion studies of cosmic-
    ray stars produced in metal foils. Phys. Rev.,
    93, 535.
Bieri, R. H. (1958) Rare gases in meteorite Car-
    bo and Copper targets exposed to 6.2 Bev pro-
    tons. Bull. Amer. Phys. Soc. Series II,3,221.

Birnbaum, M., Shapiro, M. M., Stiller B. and
O'Dell, F. W. (1952) Shape of cosmic-ray star-
size distribution in nuclear emulsions. Phys.
Rev. 86, 86.

Blau, M. and Oliver, A. K. (1956) Interaction
of 750-Mev π-mesons with emulsion nuclei. Phys.
Rev. 102, 489.

Brenner, A. E. and Williams, R. W. (1957) Cross-
section measurements near 50 Bev. Phys. Rev.
106, 1020.

Camerini, U., Fowler, P. H., Lock, W. O. and
Muirhead, H. (1950) Nuclear transmutations
produced by cosmic-ray particles of great e-
nergy. - Part IV. The distribution in energy
and the secondary interactions of the particles
emitted from stars. Phil. Mag. 41, 413.

Camerini, U., Davies, J. H., Fowler, P. H.,
Franzinetti, C., Muirhead, H., Lock, W. O.,
Perkins, D. H. and Yekutieli, G. (1951) Nuclear
transmutations produced by cosmic-ray particles
of great energy. - Part VI. Experimental results on meson production. Phil. Mag. 42,1241.

Daniel, R. R.(1957) Private Communication.

Ebert, K. H. and Wanke, H. (1957) The effects
of cosmic radiation on iron meteorites. Z.
Naturforschg. 12a, 766.

Ehmann, W. D. and Kohman, T. P. (1958a) Cosmic-
ray-induced radioactivities in meteorites.
I: Chemical and radiometric procedures for
aluminum, beryllium and cobalt. Geochim. et
Cosmochim. Acta 14, 340.

Ehmann, W. D. and Kohman, T. P. (1958b) Cosmic-
ray-induced radioactivities in meteorites.
II: Al^{26}, Be^{10} and Co^{60} in aerolites, siderites
and taktites. Geochim. et Cosmochim. Acta 14,
364.

Fireman, E. L. (1958a) Argon-39 in the Sikhote-
Alin meteorite fall. Nature (London) 181, 1613.

Fireman, E.L. and Zahringer, J. (1957) Depth
variation of tritium and argon-37 produced by
high energy protons in iron. Phys. Rev. 107,
1695.

Fireman, E. L. and De Felice, J. (1960a) Argon-
39 and tritium in meteorites. Geochim. et Cosmochim. Acta 18, 183.

Fireman, E. L. and De Felice, J. (1960b) Argon-37, argon-39 and tritium in meteorites and the spatial constancy of cosmic rays. J. Geophys. Res. 65, 3035.

Geiss, J. (1957) On the history of meteorites as deduced from isotope analysis. Chimia 11, 349.

Gentner, W. and Zahringer, J. (1957) Argon and helium as nuclear reaction products in meteorites. Geochim. et Cosmochim. Acta 11, 60.

George, E. P. and Jason, A. C. (1949) Nuclear disintegrations in photographic plates exposed to cosmic rays under lead absorbers. Proc. Phys. Soc. 62A, 243.

Gerling, E. K. and Levskii, L. K. (1956) On the origin of the rare gases in stony meteorites. Doklady Akademii Nauk, SSR 110, 750.

Gfeller, C., Herr, W., Houtermans, F. C., and Oeschger, H. (1959) Cl^{36} in meteorites. Helv. Phys. Acta 32, 277.

Hoffman, J. H. and Nier, A. O. (1958) Production of helium in iron meteorites by the action of cosmic rays. Phys. Rev. 112, 2112.

Honda, M. (1959) Cosmogenic K^{40} in iron meteorites. Geochim. et Cosmochim. Acta 17, 148.

Honda, M. and Lal, D. (1960) Some cross sections for the production of radionuclides in the bombardment of C, N, O, and Fe by medium energy protons. Phys. Rev. 118, 1618.

Honda, M., Shedlovsky, J. P., and Arnold, J. (1961) Radioactive species produced by cosmic rays in iron meteorites. Geochim. et Cosmochim. Acta 21, 133.

Ivanova, N. S., Ostroumov, V. I. and Pavlova, Yu. V. (1960) Production of multiply charged particles in photographic emulsion nuclei by 280-Mev positive pions. Soviet Phys. JETP 37, 1137.

Kohman, T. P. and Ehmann, W. D. (1958) Cosmic-ray-induced radioactivity in meteorites and tektites. Proceedings of the International Conference on Radioisotopes in Scientific Research, UNESCO, Paris (September 1957) Vol. II 661.

Lal, D., Malhotra, P. K. and Peters, B. (1958) On the production of radioisotopes in the atmosphere by cosmic radiation and their application to meteorology. Jour. Atmospheric and Terrestrial Phys. 12, 306.

Levin, B. Yu., Kozlovskaya, S. V. and Starkova, A. G. (1956) The average chemical composition of meteorites. Meteoritika 14, 38.

Martin, G. R., Thomson, S. J. and Wardle, G. (1954) Isolation and measurement of the helium-4, helium-3 and tritium produced in steel by 340 Mev proton bombardment. Phil. Mag. 45, 410.

Moskalev, V. I. and Gavrilovskii, B. V. (1957) Total cross sections for the interactions of 650 Mev. protons and nuclei. Soviet Phys. Doklady 1, 607.

Neher, H. V. (1956) Low energy primary cosmic-ray particles in (1954). Phys. Rev. 103, 228.

Neher, H. V. (1958) The primary cosmic radiation. Ann. Rev. Nucl. Sci. 8, 217.

Ostroumev, V. I. (1957) Disintegration of silver and bromine nuclei by high energy protons. Soviet Physics, JETP 5, 12.

Rudstam, G. (1955) Spallation of elements in mass range 51-75. Phil. Mag. 46, 344.

Rudstam, G. (1956) Spallation of Medium Weight Elements. Thesis, Gustaf Werner Institute for Nuclear Chemistry, University of Uppsala.

Schaeffer, O. A. and Zahringer, J. (1958) Helium and argon production in iron targets by high energy protons. Z. Naturforchg. 13a, 346.

Schaeffer, O. A. and Zahringer, J. (1959) High sensitivity mass spectrometric measurement of stable helium and argon isotopes produced by high energy protons in iron. Phys. Rev. 113, 674.

Shapiro, M. M., Stiller, B., Birnbaum, M. and O'Dell, F. W. (1951) Transition effect in lead of the star-producing radiation in the strato-sphere. I. Phys. Rev. 83, 455.

Shedlovsky, J. P. (1960) Cosmogenic Mn^{53}, Al^{26} and Be^{10} in Iron Meteorites and a Search for Terrestrial Mn^{53}, Thesis, Princeton University.

Singer, S. F. (1958) The primary cosmic radiation and its time variations. Progress in Elementary Particle and Cosmic Ray Physics. North Holland Publishing Co., Vol. IV, 205.

Sprague, A. D., Haskin, D. M., Glasser, R. G.
    and Schein, M. (1954) Analysis of 405-Mev pro-
    ton and 222-Mev negative pion stars. Phys. Rev.
    94, 994.
Sprenkel, E. L. (1959) Cosmic-Ray Produced
    Chlorine-36 in Iron Meteorites. Thesis, Uni-
    versity of Rochester (unpublished).
Sprenkel, E. L., Davis, R. and Wiig, E. O. (1959)
    Cosmic ray produced Cl^{36} and Ar^{39} in iron me-
    teorites. Bull.Amer.Phys.Soc.Series II,4,223..
Stoenner, R. W., Schaeffer, O. A. and Davis, R.
    (1960) Meteorites as space probes for testing
    the spatial constancy of cosmic radiation. J.
    Geophys. Res. 65, 3025.
Turkevich, A. and Reed, G. W. (1960) Private com-
    munication.
Urey, H. C. (1959) Primary and secondary objects.
    J. Geophys. Res. 64, 1721.
Voshage, H. and Hintenberger, H. (1959) The
    potassium isotopes as reaction products of
    cosmic radiation in the meteorite Carbo. Z.
    Naturforschg. 14a, 194.
Wanke, H. (1958) $Scandium^{45}$ as reaction product
    of cosmic rays in iron meteorites. Z. Natur-
    forschg. 13a, 645.

JAMES R. ARNOLD and **MASATAKE HONDA**
University of California, San Diego

DEVENDRA LAL
Tata Institute of Fundamental Research

Record of Cosmic-Ray Intensity

in the Meteorites

The production of measurable quantities of
He and other isotopes by cosmic-ray bombardment
in meteorites was first predicted by Bauer (1948)
and Huntley (1948). The observation by Paneth,
Reasbeck, and Mayne (1952) of a high ratio of
He3 and He4 in meteoritic He confirmed this prediction. Since then a voluminous experimental
and theoretical literature has developed in this
field.

The meteorites are targets containing a record
of the cosmic-ray bombardment to which they have
been subjected. Thus it should be possible to
obtain from them information of the past intensity of the cosmic radiation (Geiss, 1957). The
availability of new data on radioactive and
stable products (Signer and Nier, 1960 and 1961:
Honda and Arnold, 1961: and data of E.L.Fireman
et. al., O.Schaeffer et. al., and H.Wanke) has
led us to attempt a new analysis of this problem.

The first step is to calculate the relative
and absolute production rates of the observed
nuclides in meteorites using the present-day
cosmic-ray flux. If this flux has been constant

---

* Submitted to Journal of Geophysical Research
and reproduced here with the permission of the
editors.

in the past, species of half-life short compared
with the time of bombardment are in secular equilibrium. Observed rates of decay should equal
calculated production rates. Disagreement would
demonstrate a variation in cosmic-ray intensity.
The radioactive nuclide K^{40} does not appear to
be in secular equilibrium (Vashage and Hintem-
berace 1959: Honda, 1959). A comparison of the
concentrations of K^{40} with those of stable and
shorter-lived species gives us information on
the variation of the cosmic-ray flux over the
time of bombardment.

This paper will deal with iron meteorites.
Stone meteorites will not be considered here
since their complex chemical composition makes
calculation of production rates more difficult.

Method

A number of methods have been used for calculation of production rates. All employ experimental information on the cosmic radiation,
Cascade theory (Martin, 1953; Ebert and Wanke,
1957; Hoffman and Nier, 1958; Signer and Nier,
1960), the distribution of star sizes in emulsion (Shedlovsky, 1960; Goel, in press), and the
laboratory thick-target bombardment data (Fireman and Zahringer, 1957) are also employed. All
these different techniques should yield equivalent results, given the necessary data.

We have chosen to use derived spectra of primary and secondary cosmic-ray particles at 100g/
cm^2 and 10g/cm^2 depth in a meteorite. These are
combined with excitation functions to yield production rates. This method appears to us to be
the most accurate for prediction of production
rates at present. The simulated cosmic-ray bombardment technique of Fireman and Zahringer (1957),
however, may offer more promise for the future,
if the laboratory bombardment conditions are sufficiently realistic.

In meteorites below 500 kg in weight, the
change in production rate with depth is moderately small. Thus, in Grant (440 kg), the decrease
in the concentration of neon isotopes from edge
to center is 40 per cent (Signer and Nier, 1960).
Other rare gases show a smaller change. The

effect of size in the region from 20 to 500 kg
(8.5 to 25 cm radius) on production rate is also
small. This may be seen from a comparison of
data on Mn^{56}, Al^{26}, and Be^{10} in Grant, Williamstown, and Aroos (Honda and Arnold, 1961: Honda,
Shedlovsky, and Arnold, 1961), and also from
data on Ar^{39} in chondrites (Stoenner, Schaeffer
and Davis, 1960).

The choice of a standard depth of 100 g/cm^2
(13 cm) in a meteorite is a convenient one.
Many data are available for this depth in the
atmosphere. As is shown below, these can be related to the meteorite case. From a point at
this depth in a meteorite of radius 200 g/cm^2,
the distribution of distance to the surface with
angle, plotted (for example) against cosine θ
from 1 to -1, is closely similar to the distribution in a very large object on the scale of
cosine θ from 1 to 0 (upper hemisphere). Thus
the cascade development should be much the same.
We may take our reference point, then, at 100 g/
cm^2 depth in a meteorite of radius 200 g/cm^2
(mass 550 kg). The results will not be very
sensitive to this choice. We will also calculate
the spectrum at 10 g/cm^2 depth.

Because of the uncertainty in the amount of
atmospheric ablation, the calculations made for
a given depth in the preatmospheric meteorite
apply to a smaller, unknown depth in the present
object. This difficulty is not very serious if
present estimates of ablation (2 to 15 cm) are
realistic. Conversely, experimental data on
the concentration of spallation products cannot
be used to make accurate estimates of ablation.

The differential energy spectrum of nuclear-
active particles at a moderate depth in an iron
meteorite is made up of contributions of primary
and secondary particles, protons, neutrons, and
mesons (α particles are present in comparatively
small numbers). We may conclude from both experiment and theory that the energy spectrum is
continuous and monotonically decreasing in the
region of interest. The qualitative importance
of this fact may be seen in Table 1.

TABLE 1.   Content of Radioactive Nuclides in Aroos Compared with Production Cross Section in Bombardment of Fe with 730-Mev Protons

	Content in Aroos, dpm/kg	σ(exp.) 730 Mev, mb	Ratio		Content in Aroos, dpm/kg	(exp.)730 Mev,mb Ratio	
Be^{10}	4.1	1.0*	4.1	Ca^{45}	5.	1.4*	3.6
Na^{22}	2.1	0.36#	6	Sc^{46}	30.	6.4*	4.7
Al^{26}	3.6	0.43#	8	V^{49}	164	30. *	5.5
Si^{32}	0.8	0.3*	3	Cr^{51}	260	27. *	10.
Cl^{36}	14	6.8#	2.1	Mn^{51}	470	33. #	14.
Ti^{44}	4.4	2. *	2				

* M. Honda and D. Lal, to be published
# Honda and Lal (1960).

Here the cross section for the production of each species at 730 Mev. is compared with the observed decay rate in the meteorite Aroos. At both ends of the table the ratio of decay rate to cross section is high, dropping to a minimum between. For species in the Mn region, the cross section becomes high below 100 Mev. Here the importance of the low-energy particles is unmistakable. The ratio drops rather smoothly until the point is reached at which most of the production takes place in the region of 730 Mev. For products of lower Z the cross section at 730 Mev drops off, and the ratio begins to rise as production moves steadily to higher energies.

We now proceed to derive the relative energy spectra. They will then be multiplied by the best available excitation functions to give relative production rates for radioactive and

stable products. The spectra at 10 and 100 g/
cm^2 depth are then normalized using the flux of
high-energy particles and the total energy flux.
This procedure yields absolute production rates.
Finally, the constancy of the cosmic-ray intensity with time is considered.

Energy Spectrum

Primary. The composition and the energy
spectrum of primary cosmic rays are rather well
known. We made use of the data obtained by
McDonald (1959) using Cerenkov-scintillation
combination detectors. Observations during the
period of abnormally high solar activity in
1958-1959 have shown that the flux of particles
below 1 bev kinetic energy per nucleon was considerably lowered. However, the spectra for
1954-56 may be taken as typical. The solar
cycle has a large effect on the low-energy primary flux but a much smaller effect on the total
energy flux, which mainly determines the flux of
secondary particles at moderate depth. The primary differential spectrum of protons, α particles,
and heavier nuclei can be fairly well represented
by $(1 + E)^{-2.5}$ for E, the kinetic energy per
nucleon, greater than 1.5 bev. Above a given
rigidity the proportion of protons, α particles,
the C N O group, and heavier nuclei has been
found to be 103: 1.5 x 10^2: 13.3: 3.9 (McDonald,
1959; Rao, Biswas, Daniel, Neelankantan, and
Peters, 1958). At lower energies the differential spectrum falls off. The exact form is given
by McDonald for protons and a particles down to
350 Mev per nucleon. We neglect particles below this energy.

The average energy of a cosmic-ray nucleon is
found, using this spectrum, to be 4 bev. The
flux in interplanetary space near the earth can
be obtained from McDonald's data and satellite
observations (Vernov and Chudakov, 1959: Van
Allen and Frank, 1959). The latter include some
albedo particles. The total flux is 2460 parti-
cles/m^2 sec sterad. The corresponding values
for the omnidirectional energy flux is thus
20 bev/cm^2 sec.

Secondary. For simplicity we shall divide our

discussion of the secondary energy spectra into
three parts: greater than 3 bev, 100 Mev to 3
bev, and 2 Mev to 100 Mev.

The most straightforward region is that above
3 bev. A large number of experiments have shown
that in the average nuclear interaction, up to
tens of bev, a single nucleon carries away most
of the incident energy (Bogachev, Buniatov,
Merekov, Sidorov, and Yarba, 1960: Daniel, Rao,
Malhotra, and Tsuzuki, 1960: Kalbach, Lord, and
Tsao, 1960). Pi mesons carry 25 to 40 per cent
of the energy, depending on the size of the target nucleus. Low-energy nucleons share 0.3 to
0.4 bev almost independent of the primary energy.
The loss of a moderate, constant, fraction of
energy in each collision has the effect of leav-
ing the spectral shape nearly unaltered. The
near constancy of the relative spectrum in this
energy region should continue to depths much
greater than 100 g/cm^2. Even the charged π
mesons in this region are produced with the same
spectrum as that observed for primary particles
(Powell, Fowler, and Perkins, 1959). Thus the
total particle spectrum above 3 bev retains
closely the form of the primary energy spectrum.

Next, we consider the secondary particles in
the range of energy 0.1 to 3 bev. Particles in
this energy region are mostly nucleons emerging
from the cascade in the target nucleus. A fraction are charged mesons. The energy spectrum of
charged particles emerging from disintegrations
produced by cosmic rays has been studied by the
Bristol group (Powell, Fowler, and Perkins, 1959)
in nuclear emulsions exposed at high altitudes.
The number-energy spectra have been given for
all important types of charged particles. They
are found not to depend very strongly on latitude
and altitude of exposure. We assume that the
neutron energy spectrum above 100 Mev is identical with the measured production spectrum of
protons. It also seems safe to assume that the
production spectrum of nucleons in emulsion
nuclei (average Z = 30) holds good for interactions produced in iron.

Charged particles will be rendered ineffective

for nuclear reaction if they are brought to rest
by ionization. The range-energy relation in
iron is known (Atkinson, 1957), and we have calculated the probability of nuclear interaction
as a function of energy for each type of charged
particles. Thus we have estimated the production
spectrum of effective particles. Since the data
of Powell and coworkers refer to nuclear interactions well inside the atmosphere, they include
those produced by low-energy secondary particles.
The slow variation with altitude and latitude
which they find is expected to hold good so long
as the spectrum of particles above 1 bev (which
are mainly responsible for the generation of
secondaries) remains unchanged. Further down in
the atmosphere low-energy particles increase in
number. The spectrum becomes steeper, especially
in the region of 0.5 to 1 bev. At greater depths
the spectrum approaches a steady state, as is
seen in several experiments (Birnbaum, Shapiro,
Stiller, and O'Dell, 1952: Soberman, 1956; Hess,
Patterson, Wallace, and Chupp, 1959).

We may obtain the spectrum of particles in
iron from that in emulsion in the atmosphere
using the important experiment of Shapiro, Stiller, Birnbaum, and O'Dell (1951) A block of
lead roughly equivalent to a sphere of 15-cm radius was carried to a level of 22 g/cm^2 in the
atmosphere at geomagnetic latitude 56°N. Small
stacks of emulsion were placed at various points
within the block. The star size distribution in
these emulsions was compared with that in free
air. The total rate and the distribution under-
went small changes only. The changes would be
still smaller in outer space, where the incoming
flux covers 4 rather than 2 radians, although a
small "skin" effect in the outer few centimeters
due to low-energy primaries would appear.

This result justifies our use of the spectra
derived for emulsion in the atmosphere to deduce
the energy spectra of particles in an iron block.

The sum of the flux spectra of protons, neutrons, and $\pi\pm$ mesons constitutes the total spectrum of nuclear-active particles. The data of
Marquez (1952) and others show that reactions of

protons and neutrons have similar cross sections
in this region. The propriety of lumping in $\pi \pm$
mesons with nucleons is discussed in Appendix 1.

The individual spectra, and their sum, are s
shown in Figure 1. The total spectrum is well
represented by the expression $(0.2 + E)^{-2.5}$ from
0.1 to 3 bev.

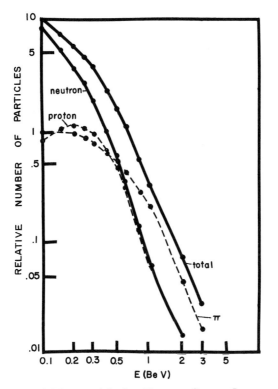

Figure 1. Differential flux of nuclear-active
particles at a depth of 100 g/cm² in a meteorite,
as deduced from data given by Powell. The contributions of protons, neutrons, and charged π
mesons are shown separately along with the total.

A check on the spectral shape can be made by
comparing (a) the observed star size distribution in nuclear emulsions exposed in the atmos-

phere at different altitudes (Birnbaum, Shapiro, Stiller, and O'Dell, 1952), and in the lead block of Shapiro, Stiller, Birnbaum, and O'Dell (1951), with (b) the star size distribution in emulsions produced by artifically accelerated particles of different energies. This procedure is described in Appendix 2. The agreement is good.

Lastly, we discuss the energy spectrum of particles from 2 to 100 Mev. This region is important for nuclides close to the target nucleus and for small fragments. Only neutrons occur in important numbers. Information can be obtained from the experimental-theoretical neutron spectrum of Hess, Patterson, Wallace, and Chupp (1959), and from the Bristol data (Powell, Fowler, and Perkins, 1959). The Bristol measurements refer to protons, and cannot be used below 20 Mev. because of Coulomb barrier effects. The results of Hess apply to light nuclei in the atmosphere. Their applicability to meteorites cannot be proved by reference to the experiment of Shapiro, Stiller, Birnbaum and O'Dell (1951), since the stars studied by them are produced almost entirely by particles above 100 Mev. The measurements of Gross (1956) on the energy spectrum (1 to 10 Mev) of neutrons arising from disintegrations in C, Al, Ni, Ag, and Au indicate that above 3 Mev. no appreciable differences exist in the neutron production spectra. Below 3 Mev the spectrum is steeper for carbon than for other targets. The Bristol and Hess curves agree above 20 Mev. As the best approximation available at present we adopt the Hess spectrum from 2 to 100 Mev. The shape of this spectrum is well represented by the expression $(1 + 0.01E^{-1} + 1.1 \times 10^{-5} E^{-2})$.

The final spectrum is given in Table 2 as $S(100,E)$. The three regions are joined smoothly, the absolute normalization is described below.

The spectrum at 10 g depth, $S(10,E)$, has also been derived. It is given in Table 2. Between 0.1 and 3 bev it has been calculated from the analysis of star size distributions mentioned above. At lower energies the curve of Hess is

TABLE 2. Energy Spectra of Nuclear-Active Particles*

Symbol	Remarks	0.002-0.1 bev	0.1-3 bev	3 bev
S(100,E)	100 g/cm² depth	$60(1 + 0.01E^{-1} + 1.1 \times 10^{-5}E{-2})$	$3.3(0.2 + E)^{-25}$	$5.8(1+E)^{-2.5}$
S(10,E)	10 g/cm² depth	$37(1 + 0.01E^{-1} + 1.1 \times 10^{-5}E{-2})$	$7.2(0.4 + E)^{-25}$	$11(1+E)^{-2.5}$
S(pr,E)	Primary spectrum		#	#

*Units are particles/cm² sec bev.
#McDonald (1959)

assumed to be valid.

EXCITATION FUNCTIONS

Excitation functions for the various product species are now required. We shall divide these into two regions: above and below 100 Mev.

Above 100 Mev, for $A < 15$, we have normalized our excitation functions at 3 bev. The values chosen are given in Table 3. Up to Be^7 experimental data are available, both for the normalization and for the shape of the excitation function. For Be^{10} the shape has been estimated, and the measured cross section at 0.73 bev has been used to fix the scale. The shape for C^{14} has been assumed the same as for Be^{10}; the cross section at 3 bev has been estimated according to Barr (1957). The normalized excitation functions are shown in Figure 2.

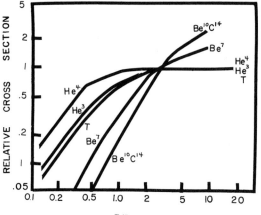

Figure 2. Assumed cross sections for the production of small nuclei from iron, normalized at 3 bev.

From $A = 20$ to $A = 54$ the shape of the excitation function is calculated from

$$\ln \sigma (E, A, Z) = \ln P - P \Delta A + C(A, Z) \qquad (1)$$

where $A = 56 - A$ and $P = 0.11E^{-0.64}$ (see Appendix 3). This equation is fairly consistent with the shape of the excitation function above 0.1 bev where data are available. We have normalized

TABLE 3. Cross sections Assumed for
Normalization of Excitation Functions

	mb	Reference		mb	Reference
		3 Bev			
H^3	90	f,k,n,o,p,q	Be^7	13	a,c,d
He^3	200	e,f,s	Be^{10}	7	b
He^4	650	e,f,s	C^{14}	3	
		1 Bev			
Ne^{20}	1.6	e,f,r	K^{41}	16	r
Ne^{21}	1.6	e,f,r	Ca^{41}	7	
Ne^{22}	1.6	e,f,r	Ca^{42}	18	r
Na^{22}	0.70	a,d,g,h,i	Ca^{43}	20	r
Al^{26}	0.76	a	Ca^{44}	22	r
Si^{32}	0.4	b	Ca^{45}	1.5	b,h
P^{32}	3.1	d,g	Ca^{46}	0.2	
P^{33}	2.2	d,g	Sc^{45}	25	r
Cl^{36}	7.5	a	Sc^{46}	7.0	b,h
Ar^{35}	9.0	e,f,r	Ti^{44}	2	b
Ar^{37}	5.0	e,f,k	V^{48}	25	h
Ar^{38}	12	e,f,r	V^{49}	30	b,h
Ar^{39}	6.4	e,f	V^{50}	14	
Ar^{40}	2.5		Cr^{51}	25	b,h
Ar^{42}	0.06	b,j	Mn^{52}	10	a,h,m
K^{39}	13	r	Mn^{53}	30	
K^{40}	10	b	Mn^{54}	30	a
			Fe^{55}	50	l

a Honda and Lal (1960).
b M. Honda and D. Lal, to be published.
c Baker, Friedlander and Hudis (1958).
d Barr (1957).
e Schaeffer and Zahringer (1959).
f Goebel and Zahringer, in press.
g Friedlander, Miller, Wolfgang, Hudis, and Baker (1954).
h Rudstam, Stevenson, and Folger (1952).
i Batzel, Miller, and Seaborg (1951).
j Stoenner, Schaeffer, and Davis (1960).
k Fireman and Zahringer (1957).
l Markowitz, Rowland, and Friedlander (1958).
m Reeder and Markowitz, unpublished.
n Currie, Libby, and Wolfgang (1956).
o Currie (1959).
p Bieri (1958).
q Fireman (1955).
r From Appendix 3, formula A5.
s J. Zahringer, private communication

each curve at 1 bev, using experimental data
for proton bombardment of Fe where available,
data on targets of similar Z (often Cu), formula
A5 in Appendiz 3 for cumulative cross sections,
or where necessary the Rudstam equation (Rudstam,
1956; Honda and Lal, 1960). The values used for
normalization are shown in Table 3. For Fe^{55}
the Cu^{53} (p, pn) Cu^{62} curve has been used(Markowitz, Rowland, and Firedlander, 1958).

Below 100 Mev the bombarding particles are
mainly neutrons. Here very few experimental
data are available. The cross section for He^4
is certainly large down nearly to the (n, a)
threshold, and for H^3 and He^3 it may be. The
values assumed are arbitrary. For A 48 we
have used the excellent data of Sharp, Diamond,
and Wilkinson (1956) for protons on Co^{59}. The
cross section for Fe^{56} (n, xp, yn) is assumed
equal to that of Co^{59} (p, xp, yn). This procedure is also arbitrary but systematic. Sharp
and co-workers present evidence that it is reliable to about a factor of 2, except where the
product has a magic number of neutrons or protons, when the experimental cross section is low.
This applies to Mn^{53}, but no correction has been
made. The data of Ashby, Catron, Newkirk, and
Taylor (1958) on $Fe^{56}(n,2n)Fe^{55}$, and data of
Hughes and Schwartz (1958) on $Cu^{63}(n,2n)Cu^{62}$
have been used to obtain the excitation function
for Fe^{55}.

The estimation of excitation functions for
Fe^{60} and Co and Ni isotopes is discussed in
Appendix 4.

RELATIVE PRODUCTION RATES

The relative production of each species is
given by

$$R(X,A,Z) = \int \sigma (E,A,Z) \ S(X,E) \ dE =$$

$$\int \sigma (E,A,Z)(ES(X,E)) \ d \ln E \quad (2)$$

For convenience, ln E has been used as the
independent variable in the actual numerical in-
tegrations. The results are given in Table 5.

TABLE 4. Assumed Cross Sections* below 100 Mev, in mb

Nuclide	2	2.8	4	5.7	8	11	16	22	31	44	62	87	Target Nuclide
H3							2.5	5	5	5	5	5	Fe56
He3							5	10	10	10	10	10	Fe56
He4							50	100	100	100	100	100	Fe56
V48											1	8	Fe56
V49										4	4	10	Fe56
V50											4	6	Fe56
Cr51									17	67	30	30	Fe56
Mn52									6	9	9	9	Fe56,Fe54
Mn53							9	36	34	48	90	55	Fe56,Fe54
Mn54		1.5	3	5	5	6	3	2	40	140	65	45	Fe56,Fe54
Fe55						10	770	580	340	230	150	100	Fe56,Fe54
Fe60									0.1	0.3	0.2	0.1	Ni64,Ni62
Co56							1	3	13	20	9	6	Ni58,Co59
Co57							8	10	10	7	6	4	Ni58,Co59
Co58	4	7	6	10	13	16	19	23	18	11	5	3	Ni58,Co59
Co60					1	2	2	1	3	2	1	1	Ni58,Co59,Ni60
Ni59							1	3	3	2	1	1	Ni60

E (Mev)

*These are cumulative cross sections. Neutron capture processes are not included. The cross sections for production are based on total Fe. For the Co and Ni isotopes they are based on total Fe, assuming 6.5 per cent Ni and 0.43 per cent Co (Honda and Arnold, 1961). The $Fe54(n,p)Mn54$ excitation function is taken as that of $Fe56(n,p)Mn56$ (Hughes and Schwartz, 1958), lowered by 3 Mev.

TABLE 5   Production Rates Relative to Cl^{36}

Nuclide	Aroos Expt*	S(100)	S(10)	S(pr)
H^3		12	10	8
He^3	34'	27	23	17
He^4	128'	135	108	63
Be^7		0.69	0.74	1.0
Be^{10}	0.29	0.31	0.34	0.62
C^{14}		0.13	0.15	0.27
Ne	1.2'	0.73	0.81	1.3
Na^{22}	0.15	0.11	0.12	0.18
Al^{26}	0.26	0.10	0.11	0.15
Si^{32}	0.06	0.05	0.06	0.06
P^{32}		0.41	0.44	0.49
P^{33}		0.30	0.32	0.35
Cl^{36}	(1)	(1)	(1)	(1)
Ar^{36}	(1.2)'	1.2	1.2	1.2
Ar^{37}	1.3"	0.65	0.65	0.61
Ar^{38}	1.9'	1.6	1.5	1.4
Ar^{39}	0.9-1.0"	0.90	0.85	0.74
Ar^{40}		0.38	0.35	0.31
Ar^{42}		0.11	0.09	0.08
K^{39}		1.8	1.7	1.5
K^{40}	0.6#	1.5	1.4	1.2
K^{41}		2.6	2.3	1.8
Ca^{41}		1.1	1.0	0.8
Ca^{42}		3.1	2.6	1.9
Ca^{43}	3.9$	3.6	3.0	2.0
Ca^{44}		4.2	3.5	2.1
Ca^{45}	0.3	0.28	0.22	0.13
Ca^{46}	0.09$	0.05	0.04	0.02
Sc^{45}		5.0	4.0	2.3
Sc^{46}	2.1	1.5	1.2	0.63
Ti^{44}	0.31	0.38	0.31	0.19
V^{48}	6	7.3	5.2	2.2
V^{49}	12	9.6	6.7	2.6
V^{50}	10$	5.2	3.5	1.2
Cr^{51}	20	19	11	2.0
Mn^{52}		6.6	4.2	0.8
Mn^{53}	38	33	18	2.5
Mn^{54}	34	38	20	2.5
Fe^{55}	120¢	220	100	6.2
Fe^{60}		0.1	0.1	0.03
Co^{56}	(4.4)	4.5	2.1	0.1
Co^{57}	6.4	5.5	3.0	0.6
Co^{58}	(4.4)	17	7.8	0.1
Co^{60}	1.3	0.6	0.3	0.01
Ni^{59}	3.4	1.4	0.7	0.1

* Honda and Arnold (1961), unless otherwise noted.
' Rare-gas data are from Signer and Nier (1961).
" Fireman and DeFelice (1960); Wanke, unpublished; Heymann and
                                        Schaeffer (1961).
¢ Activity 1600 ± 600 dpm/kg from M. Honda, unpublished.
Calculated from the value 7.8 ± 0.5 obtained by Stauffer and
                    Honda (1961) and unpublished data.

These are normalized to $Cl^{36} = 1$. The yields
are cumulative where appropriate (e.g., $Ar36$
includes $Cl36$; $Ar40$ includes $Cl40$ but not $K40$).
The experimental data for the radioactive species
in the iron meteorite Aroos (Honda and Arnold,
1961) are given for comparison. The species
Be^{10}, $Al26$, and $Mn53$ have the same abundance in
Grant and Williamstown as in Aroos within 20 per
cent or less (Honda, Shedlowsky, and Arnold,
1961). Values for the rare-gas isotopes in
Aroos, normalized to $Ar^{36} = 1.2$, are also given.

The contribution of particles below 100 Mev
to the production of each species is given in
Table 6. In extreme cases such as Co^{58} and Fe^{55}
this contribution is of the order of 90 per
cent of the total.

In addition to the calculation given in Table
5, we have made some estimates of the production
rates at depths of 500 to 1000 g/cm^2 in a large
meteorite. We estimate that the ratio $\lesssim Ne/Ar^{36}$
will be about 30 per cent higher. Such species
as Mn^{56}, however, produced mainly by low-energy
neutrons, will increase relative to Ar^{36} by
factors of 3 to 5.

A further comparison can be made with results
of Wanke (1960) on stable cosmogenic Sc^{45}. He
finds the ratio Sc^{45}/Ne^{22} nearly constant at
18-20 in several meteorites. From this the experimental ratio $Sc^{45}/\lesssim Ne$ may be given as 6-7.

ABSOLUTE ENERGY SPECTRA AND PRODUCTION RATES

The energy spectra at 100 and 10 g/cm^3 depth
can be normalized in a number of different ways.
Two methods appear to us most reliable for this
purpose: using the flux of particles of $E \geqslant 3$
bev, and using the total energy flux.

First we must consider the effect of complex
nuclei. The mean free paths of these nuclei are
smaller than that of protons, and the general
effect of nuclear collision is that the bombarding nucleus breaks up (complete breakup of
heavier nuclei will take more than one collision).
Below 50 g/cm^2 depth in the meteorite we assume
that the flux is the same as it would be if all
the primary nucleons entered the meteorite as
free particles. The effect of this assumption

TABLE 6.   Production by Particles below 100 Mev
           (Relative to total Cl^{36})

Nuclide	S(100*)	Nuclide	S(100)
H^3	1	Mn^{53}	20
He^3	2	Mn^{54}	25
He^4	18	Fe^{55}	190
V^{48}	0.9	Fe^{60}	0.01
V^{49}	1.3	Co^{56}	3.9
V^{50}	0.8	Co^{57}	3.1
Cr^{51}	10	Co^{58}	17
Mn^{52}	2.5	Co^{60}	0.6
		Ni^{59}	1.0

* To obtain relative production by particles
below 100 Mev for S(10) multiply by 0.44.

is to overestimate the flux somewhat, but no
data are available for a correction. At a depth
of 10 g/cm² the error introduced by this assumption is somewhat larger, but since it is of
major significance only for particles coming
from one hemisphere the difference will not be
great.

The fact that one nucleon carries away a major fraction of the energy in collisions in the
bev region is discussed under "Energy Spectrum"
above. The inelasticity, defined as the energy
carried by π mesons in the laboratory system,
is around 0.3 for air and 0.5 for iron (Babayan,
Grigorov, Dubrovin, Mischenkov, Murzin, Sarycheva, Sobiniakiv, and Rapoport, 1959). The probability of emitting a π meson of energy greater
than 3 bev is appreciable only above about 20

bev incident nucleon energy. About 0.4 bev is
carried by evaporation and low-energy cascade
nucleons. Since the primary flux falls rapidly
with energy the situation is simplified for
distances of one or two mean free paths. We
need only consider the production of fast nucleons by the primaries. The rate of decrease
of the flux of nucleons of $E > 3$ bev can be calculated, on the reasonable assumption that the
emerging nucleon moves in the forward hemisphere
relative to the direction of the primary.
being defined as the mean free path for nuclear
interaction, and   as the mean free path for
decrease of the high-energy flux, it can be
shown that

$$1 - (\lambda_{int}/\lambda_{abs}) = (1-K)^S \qquad (3)$$

where K=inelasticity and S=slope of the integral
primary spectrum. For iron, λ_{abs} is approximately equal to 1.5 λ_{int}. The uncertainty in
this value is less than 20 per cent. The interaction mean free path in iron in 100 g/cm^2,
which corresponds to $\lambda_{abs} = 150$ g/cm^2. Integration over angle for our standard meteorite
at 100 g/cm^2 depth yields the result that the
flux of particles of $E \geq 3$ bev is reduced to
0.25 of the original value. An error in the
value of λ_{abs} can be considered as an error in
the coordinates of our assumed standard depth.

The coefficient of S(100) above 3 bev is determined from this result and the primary spectrum. The coefficients in the lower energy
ranges are determined by the condition of con-
tinuity.

Integration of the spectrum S(100,E) using
this normalization yields the result that 60
per cent of the total energy present in the primary beam is retained at this depth. The remaining 40 per cent corresponds to losses in the
form of ionization π^o mesons, and escape of particles from the meteorite.

Two approaches have been taken to obtain an
independent estimate of the energy loss to this
depth. First we consider the differences in the
total energy carried by the particles in the
production spectrum given by the Bristol group,

and that of the effective spectrum obtained
after correction for ionization losses, π^{o} mesons,
escape, and minor effects. An approximate value
of 45 per cent is obtained for the energy loss..
Another estimate may be based on the discussion
of energy balance in the atmosphere given by
Puppi (1956). A correction is made for the fact
that $\pi^{\pm}$ mesons, which do not interact in the atmosphere, are usually effective in the meteorite. By estimating energy losses by his procedure, a value of 40 per cent is derived. Both
estimates agree well with the value obtained
above.

The total number of nuclear-active particles
at this depth may also be derived. The value
obtained is 16 particles per incident primary.
Of these about 80 per cent are neutrons below
100 Mev. This figure seems reasonable on the
basis of the Bristol data (Powell, Fowler, and
Perkins, 1959).

The spectrum at 10 g/cm^2 may also be normalized in the same way. In a meteorite of radius
25 cm the calculated reduction in the flux of
high-energy particles (integrated over 4 is 50
per cent.

The rate of production, in atoms/min kg, is
given by

$$R = \frac{6.0 \cdot 10^{23} \times 10^3 \times 60}{} \int S\sigma\, dE = 0.65 \int S\sigma\, dE \quad (4)$$

where σ is expressed in millibarns. The absolute
production rate of Cl^{36} for S(100) is 23 dpm/kg.
For S(10) and S(pr) the rates are calculated to
be 34 and 35 dpm/kg, respectively. The absolute
rates of production for all other species in
Table 5 can be obtained by multiplying by these
factors.

The value of 23 dpm/kg Cl^{36} may be compared
with the experimental figure of 14 dpm/kg in
Aroos. The difference, a factor of 0.6, may
well be within the combined error of the absolute
flux normalization and the excitation function.
It is also possible that the result would be
better if the effect of atmospheric ablation of
the meteorite could be included. The important
conclusion is that an absolute flux equal to or

lower than the experimental one is sufficient to produce all the species considered.

We may now consider the depth effect in the production of rare gases. The change in production of rare gases with depth in Grant (440 kg present mass) may be compared with calculated values, for the limiting case of zero atmospheric ablation. This is done in Table 7, using data obtained by Signer and Nier (1960) for two points at approximately 10 and 100 g/cm^2 present depth. It appears that some ablation has taken place, although the amount is very difficult to estimate.

TABLE 7.   Observed and Calculated Depth Effect
           in Grant*
           (Limiting case of zero ablation)
              $C(10)/C(100)$

Nuclide	Observed[+]	Calculated
He^3	1.19	1.3
He^4	1.08	1.2
$\leq Ne$	1.32	1.6
Ar^{36}	1.28	1.5
Ar^{36}	1.23	1.4

*Signer and Nier (1960)
+Sample S-71a, bar N, is compared to sample S-47, bar J.

DISCUSSION

Study of Table 5 shows that the agreement between the calculated and observed values for the relative production rates of various stable and radioactive species is very good. The average deviation for each species (except Al^{26} and Co and Ni isotopes) is about 30 per cent. The high observed values of Al^{26} are presumably due to the bombardment of P and S in the meteorites. The trends in production rates are accurately reproduced. In particular the factor of about 1000 between the production rates of Fe^{55} and Na^{22} is seen to come about because of

the abundance of low-energy particles in the
secondary spectrum. Although depth effects are
not explored in detail, the agreement is good,
allowing for some ablation. It should be noted
that our model predicts a sharp increase with
depth for $A \geqslant 53$, increases persisting down to
$A = 48$.

By far the largest discrepancy is that for
Co^{58}. Even if the entire observed yield of Co^{56}
+ 58 is assigned to this species, the prediced
value is high by a factor of 3. The production
of this species is mainly by Ni^{58} (n,p) Co^{58}.
For this type of reaction nearly all production
occurs in the region of the peak, below 50 Mev.
At high energies the cross section becomes very
small. The experimental value of 560 $\pm$ 110 mb
at 14 Mev (Purser and Titterton, 1958) has been
used to normalize the Fe^{56} (n,p) Mn^{56} cross-
section curve, which peaks at 14 Mev. There is
also a low-energy contribution, and one from
Co^{59} (n,2n) Co^{58}. The calculation for Fe^{56} de-
viates by a smaller amount in the same direction.
Perhaps the flux at energies 14 Mev has been
overestimated. The species Co^{60} and Ni^{59} can
also be produced by the (n,) process (Van
Dilla, Arnold, and Anderson, 1960). This production has not been included in Table 5. It
will be discussed in a separate paper.

The success of the model in predicting decay
rates for the species of short half-life is
evidence for its applicability.

Its equal success in predicting the decay
rates of the long-lived species Be^{10}, Al^{26}, Si^{32},
Cl^{36}, Ti^{44}, and Mn^{53} is strong evidence of the
constancy of the cosmic-ray flux over the last
few million years. More precisely, we consider
the average quantity.

$$\int_0^T \int_0^\infty S(E,X,t)\, \sigma(E,A,Z)\ e^{-\lambda(A,Z)t} dE\ dt$$

Where t is reckoned positive backward from the
time of fall, and T is the time when bombardment
commenced. This integral appears to have the

same value, within at most a factor of 2, for
each radioactive product species considered.
Such a statement does not preclude the possibility of short, intense bursts of cosmic radiation
(or solar radiation), provided that the integral
is not much affected.

Any variation in the cosmic-ray bombardment
over periods of the order of 10^8 to 10^9 years
can only be studied using cosmogenic K^{40}. This
may be done by comparing bombardment ages obtained using K^{40} and a stable specie with those
obtained with a shorter-lived radioactive nuclide and a stable one. The pairs K^{40}-K^{41} and
Cl^{36}-Ar^{36} are good examples. The same age
should be obtained from both pairs, if the
bombardment intensity has been constant. If the
K^{40} content is relatively lower, and thus the
K^{40}-K^{41} age longer, the level of bombardment was
lower in the past, and the true duration longer
than that derived from such pairs as Cl^{36}-Ar^{36}.
As in the case of Williamstown (Honda, Shedlovsky,
and Arnold, 1961), the question of terrestrial
age of the meteorite must be considered if the
meteorite is a "Find."

At present the data are fragmentary. The
direct measurement of the ratio K^{40}/K^{41} by
Voshage and Hintenberger (1959) yielded the result that Carbo is 0.4 to 1.3 X 10^9 years older
than Treysa. Other pairs have given 5 X 10^8 and
7 to 12 X 10^8 years for Treysa and Carbo (Sprenkel, 1959; Vilcsek, Wanke, 1961) respectively.

According to Honda (1959) the absolute concentrations of cosmogenic K^{40} in Grant and Williamstown are consistent with the bombardment ages of
about 5 X 10^8 years obtained from other pairs
(Schaeffer and Zahringer, 1960; Heymann and
Schaeffer, 1961; Honda, Shedlovsky, and Arnold,
1961). For Aroos, ages of 5.9 and 5.4 X 10^8
years have been reported (Heymann and Schaeffer,
1961, Vilcsek, Wanke, 1961) using Cl^{36}-Ar^{36} and
Cl^{36}-Ne. The value of 2.3 dpm/kg reported by
Honda and Arnold (1961) is definitely lower than
predicted from these ages. Recently Stauffer
and Honda (1961) have made a new mass-spectro-
metric determination, using K^{39} carrier. They

obtained 4.9×10^{-10} g/g or 7.8 ± 0.5 dpm/kg.
The older result must be attributed to loss of
K, at extremely low concentration, in the chemical processing. The present value is consistent
with the predictions of Table 5.

These facts suggest, but do not yet prove,
that even over the past 0.5 to 1×10^9 years the
level of cosmic-ray intensity has been similar
to the present one.

The observed constancy of the cosmic-radiation
intensity over various periods up to millions of
years is to be expected on the basis of current
theories of cosmic-ray origin (Ginzburg, 1958;
Hayakawa, Ito and Terashima, 1958; Hayakawa,
1959). Theoretical predictions concerning variations on a 10^9-year time scale are not easy to
make. In the theory of Shklovsky and Ginzburg,
type I supernovae play an essential role. Since
these occur in our galaxy at the rate of about
one every hundred years, and since the life of
each cosmic-ray particle in the galaxy is much
longer, the fluctuations should be averaged out.
However, a change in the rate of production of
cosmic rays by type in the rate of production of
cosmic rays by type I supernovac in the galaxy
in 10^9 years is quite possible. Similar considerations apply to other theories. Since 10^9
years is an appreciable fraction of the life of
the galaxy.

APPENDIX 1. π MESONS

Some differences exist in the excitation functions of isotopes for π mesons and protons. The
available literature suggests that in the bev
region the size distribution of π^- produced star
resembles very closely that of proton stars. At
lower energies, however, the situation is not
quite clear. Analyses of π^- produced stars in
nuclear emulsions have been made at 35-50, 70-
80, 220, and 280 and 750 Mev (Blau and Oliver,
1956; Ivanova, Ostroumov, and Pavlova, 1960;
Sprague, Haskin, Glasser, and Schein, 1954;
Bernardini and Levy, 1951). The results would
seem to indicate a somewhat steeper star size
distribution than for protons of kinetic energy
equal to the total π^- energy. At low energies,

the only results on π^+ stars are in the region
35-80 Mev (Sprague, Haskin, Glasser, and Schein,
1954). Here we find that the π^+ star size distribution is flatter than that of protons. If
we take an equal proportion of π^+ and π^- in the
meteorite, the resulting star size distribution
seems to be very similar to that for proton
stars. Qualitatively, we conclude that isotope
excitation functions for combined π^- mesons and
protons are similar.

We have not considered the reactions induced
by π^- capture at rest. Radiochemical analyses
have been made in iodine (Winsberg, 1954) and
bromine (Sugihara and Libby, 1952). This combined with nuclear emulsion data would suggest
that about 30 per cent of stars are zero-pronged
(emission of neutrons only). The size distribution of stars is similar to that of proton stars
induced by 200 Mev protons. The π^- capture e-
vents can therefore be considered to be equivalent to a flux of 200 Mev protons. The average
number of slow π^- mesons produced per star in
iron is less than 15 per cent (Bernardizi and
Levy, 1951). This is equivalent to raising the
flux of neutrons in the energy region 100 to
300 Mev by less than 20 per cent. We neglect
this effect.

APPENDIX 2.   STAR SIZE DISTRIBUTIONS

Star size distributions for incident beams of
monoenergetic protons have been determined at
numerous points between 0.1 and 6 bev, for number of prongs $n \geq 3$ (Lock, March, Muirhead and
Rosser, 1955; Morand, Baudinet-Robinet, and
Winand, 1958). Morand and co-workers have fitted the experimental distributions with an empirical equation. With the aid of this equation
we have obtained the integral star size distributions at energies throughout the region of
interest, spaced at a constant logarithmic in-
terval. A crude by adequate estimate of   (E),
the total cross section for production of stars
of three or more prongs, is made using the data
of Germain (1951) for stars of $n \geq 2$,   and cor-
recting for three-pronged stars. σ_3 drops to a
low value below 100 Mev and approaches constancy

at bev energies.

For a given differential energy spectrum of star-producing radiation S(X,E), the integral star size distribution may be calculated from

$$T(n) = \int I(E,n)\sigma(E)S(X,E)dE$$
$$= \int I(E,n)\sigma(E)(ES(X,E)d \ln E \quad (A1)$$

This distribution may be compared with the experimental one, or the function S can be varied until a good fit is obtained.

The function T(n) as given by Birnbaum, Shapiro, Stiller, and O'Dell (1952) for a depth of 50 g/cm^2 in the atmosphere is plotted in Figure 3 along with the function derived from the distribution S(100,E). The distribution S(10,E) in the region 0.1 to 3 bev was derived used equation A1.

APPENDIX 3.   SHAPE OF EXCITATION
FUNCTION ABOVE 100 Mev

We assume that the total inelastic scattering cross section is constant throughout the region of interest, and that

$$\sum_{28}^{56}\sigma(A) = \sigma_{in}$$

We further assume that

$$\ln\sigma(E,A) = PA - q(E) \quad (A2)$$

and that the distribution of $\sigma(z)$ among isobars is independent of E. From these assumptions we may conclude, for any E,

$$\sum_{A=28}^{56} e^{PA-q} = e^{-q} \sum_{A=28}^{56} e^{PA}$$

$$= \frac{e^{56P} - e^{27P}}{e^{q}(1 - e^{-P})} = \sigma_{in} \quad (A3)$$

We approximate by setting $(1 - e^{-P}) = P$ and neglecting e^{27P}, a procedure that does not introduce large errors in the region of interest.

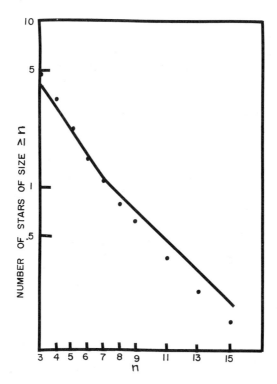

Figure 3.   Comparison of experimental and cal-
mulated relative integral star size distributions
in emulsion at 100 g/cm² depth. The line gives
smoothed experimental data: points are calculated.

Then
$$\ln \sigma_{in} = 56P - q - \ln P \quad (A4)$$
Eliminating q,
$$\ln \sigma(E,A) = \ln P - P\Delta A + \ln \sigma_{in} \quad (A5)$$
Where $\Delta A = 56 - A$, while
$$\ln \sigma(E,A,Z) = \ln P - P\Delta A + C (A,Z) \quad (A6)$$
We have derived $P = 0.11E^{-0.64}$ from published
data for protons of 0.34 to 6 bev on Cu, using
R = 1.8 and S = 0.469 for spallation products in
the region $(Z - SA) \leqslant 1.5$ (Rudstam, 1956). A

similar relation was used earlier for Fe (Honda, Lal, 1960).

The approximations used (and the assumption of constant σ_{in} throughout the energy region) introduce appreciable errors. However, the simple equation A6 fits the available data as well as any more exact expression we have used. We believe it to be adequate from A = 20 to A = 54. It has the great advantage of reducing the subjective element in the selection of experimental cross-section data.

APPENDIX 4.   Ni and Co CROSS SECTIONS

The cross sections for Ni and Co isotopes are sums of cross sections for production from stable Ni and Co species. Processes like (p, xn) or (π^+, x) or Fe are unimportant. All cross sections from Co^{59} were assumed equal to those for production of the same species by protons (Sharp, Diamond, and Wilkinson, 1956). These were normalized to an abundance of 0.4 per cent Co. Ni^{58}.(n,p) Co^{58} was taken from experiment below 4 Mev and at 14 Mev (Purser and Titterton, 1958). Ni^{60} (n,p) Co^{60} was taken as the same as Fe^{56} (n,p) Mn^{56} (Hughes and Schwartz, 1958). Co^{57} from Ni^{58} was taken as twice Ni^{58} (n, 2n) Ni^{57} (Hughes and Schwartz, 1958) at low energy, or twice Cu^{63} (p, pn)(Markowitz et al 1958) at high. Co^{56} from Ni^{58} was assumed equal to twice Mn^{54} from Fe^{56}, because of cumulative yield. Cross sections for Co^{58}, Co^{60}, and Ni^{59} were estimated similarly. For Co^{60} and Fe^{60} higher isotopes of Ni were also considered.

Acknowledgments

This research was supported by the Office of Ordnance Research, U. S. Army, and the National Aeronautics and Space Administration. We are grateful to R. R. Daniel, Rams, A. Subranianiam, and many other colleagues for helpful discussions, and to Margaret Cassidy for assistance in the calculations.

REFERENCES

Ashby, V.J., H.C.Catron, L.L. Newkirk, and C.J. Taylor, 1953. Absolute measurement of (n,2n) cross sections at 14.1 m.e.v. Phys. Rev.111, 616.

Atkinson, J. H. 1957. High energy particle data, II. U C R L-2426.

Babayan, C.P., N.L. Grigorov, M.M. Dubrovin, L. G. Mischenkov, V.S.Murzin, L.I. Sarycheva, V. S. Sobiniakiv, and I.D. Rapoport. 1959. Proc. Moscow Cosmic Ray Conf., 1, 178.

Baker, E., G. Friedlander, and J. Hudis, 1958. Formation of Be7 in interactions of various nuclei with high energy protons. Phys. Rev., 112, 1319.

Barr, D.L. 1957. AEC Rept. U C R L - 3793.

Barzel, R.E., D.R.Miller, and G.T.Seaborg. 1951. High Energy spallation products of Cu. Phys. Rev., 84, 671.

Bauer, C.A. 1947. Production of He in meteorites by cosmic radiation. Phys. Rev., 72, 354.

Bauer, C.A. 1948a. Absorption of cosmic radiation in meteorites. Phys. Rev. 74, 225.

Bauer, C.A. 1948b. Rate of production of He in meteorites by cosmic radiation. Phys. Rev. 74, 501.

Bernardini, G. and F. Levy. 1951. Capture and scattering of mesons. Phys. Rev. 84, 610.

Bieri, R. 1958. Bull. Am. Phys. Soc.(2) 3, 221.

Birnbaum, M., M. M. Shapiro, B. Stiller, and F. W. O'Dell. 1952. Cosmic-ray star-size distributions in nuclear emulsions. Phys. Rev. 86,86.

Blau, M. and A.K. Oliver. 1956. Interaction of 750 m.e.v. π mesons with emulsion nuclei. Phys. Rev. 102, 489.

Bogachev, N.P., S.A. Buniatov, V.P. Merekov, V. M. Sidorov, and V.A. Yarba, 1960. J. Exptl. Theoret. Phys. USSR, 38(9), 1346.

Currie, L. A. 1959. Tritium production by 6-b.e. v. protons. Phys. Rev. 114, 878.

Currie, L. A., W.F. Libby, and R.L. Wolfgang. 1956. T production by high energy protons. Phys. Rev. 101, 1557.

Daniel, R.R., N. Kameswara Rao, P.K. Malhotra,

and B.Y. Tsuzuki. 1960. Nuovo cimento, 16,1.

Ebert, K. H., and H. Wanke. 1957. Ueber die Einwerkung der Hohenstrahlung auf Eisenmeteorite, Z. Naturforsch. 12a, 766.

Fireman, E.L. 1955. Tritium production by 2.2-b.e.v. protons on Fe and its relation to cosmic radiation. Phys. Rev., 97, 1303.

Fireman, E.L. and J. Zahringer, 1957, Depth Variation of Tritium and Argon -37 Produced by High-Energy Protons in Iron. Phys. Rev. 107, 1695.

Fireman, E.L., and J. de Felice. 1960. Ar^{39} and T in meteorites. J. Geophys. Research 65, 3035.

Friedlander, G., J. M. Miller, R. Wolfgang, J. Hudis, and E. Baker. 1954. Nuclear Reactions of Copper with 2.2 Bev. Protons. Phys. Rev. 94, 727.

Geiss, J. 1957. The History of Meteorites from isotope measurement. Chimia (Switz.) 11,349.

Germain, L.S. 1951. Stars in Photographic Emulsions Initiated by Protons. Phys. Rev. 82,596.

Ginzburg, V.I. 1958. Progress in Elementary Particle and Cosmic Ray Physics, vol. 4. chapter 5.

Goebel, K. and J. Zahringer, in press.

Goel, P.S., Geochim. et Cosmochim Acta in press.

Gross, E. 1956. The absolute yield of low-energy neutrons from 190 Mev proton bombardment of gold, silver, nickel, aluminum and carbon, Thesis. U C R L - 330.

Hayakawa, S., K. Ito, and Y. Teraskima. 1958. Prog. Theoret. Phys. Suppl. 6, 1.

Hayakawa, S., and M. Koshiba. 1959. Prog. Theoret. Phys. 21, 473.

Hess, W.N., H.W. Patterson, R. Wallace, and E.L. Chupp. 1959. Cosmic-Ray Neutron Energy Spectrum. Phys. Rev. 116, 445.

Heymann, D. and O.A. Schaeffer. Abstracts, 92nd Ann. Meeting Am. Geophys. Union. Washington, D.C., April 1961.

Hoffman, J.H., and A.O. Nier. 1958. Production of Helium in Iron Meteorites by the Action of Cosmic Rays. Phys. Rev. 112, 2112.

Honda, M. 1959. Cosmogenic potassium 40 in iron meteorites. Geochim. et Cosmochim. Acta. 17,148.

Honda, M. and J.R. Arnold. Radioactive species produced by cosmic rays in the Aroos iron meteorite. Geochim. et Cosmochim. Acta 23, 219.

Honda, M., and D. Lal. 1960. Some Cross Sections for the Production of Radio-Nuclides in the Bombardment of C,N,O, and Fe by Medium Energy Protons. Phys. Rev. 118, 1618.

Honda, M., J.P. Shedlovsky, and J.R. Arnold, Radioactive species produced by cosmic rays in iron meteorites. Geochim. et Cosmochim. Acta. 22,133.

Hughes, D.J. and R.B. Schwartz. Neutron cross sections. AEC Report BNL325, 2nd edition.

Huntley, H.E. 1948. Production of helium by cosmic rays. Nature, 161, 356.

Ivanova, N.S., V.I. Ostroumov, and Yu. V. Pavlova. 1961. Soviet Phys. JETP, 37, 1137.

Kalbach, R.M., J. J. Lord, and C.H. Tsao. 1959. Elastic Proton-Proton Collisions at 6.2 Bev in Nuclear Emulsions. Phys. Rev. 113, 325.

Lock, W.O., P.V. March, H. Muirhead, and W.G.V. Rosser. 1955. Nuclear interactions of 950-m. e.v. protons. Proc. Roy. Soc. London, A.230,215.

Markowitz, S., F.S. Rowland, and G. Friedlander. 1958. (p,pn) Reactions at Proton Energies from 0.3 to 3.0 Bev. Phys. Rev. 112, 1295.

Marquez, L. 1952. Spallation of Cu with High Energy Neutrons. Phys. Rev. 88, 225.

Martin, G.R. 1953. Recent Studies on Iron Meteorites. IV The origin of meteoritic helium and the age of meteorites. Geochim. et Cosmochim. Acta 3, 288.

McDonald, F.B. 1959. Primary Cosmic-Ray Intensity near Solar Maximum. Phys. Rev. 116, 462.

Morand, M., Y. Baudinet-Robinet, and L. Winand. 1958. Nuclear disintegrations produced in nuclear emulsions by 4 and 6 b.e.v. protons. Proc. 2nd Intern. Conf. Geneva, 30, 109.

Paneth, F.A., P. Reasbeck, and K. I. Mayne. 1952. Helium 5 content and age of meteorites. Geochim. et Cosmochim. Acta, 2, 300.

Powell, C.F., P.H. Fowler, and D.H. Perkins. 1959. The Study of Elementary Particles by the Photographic Method, 442. Pergamon Press, New York.

Puppi, G. 1956. The energy balance of cosmic

radiation. Progr. in Cosmic Ray Phys. 3.

Purser, K.H., and E.W. Titterton. 1958. Ni^{58} (n,p)Co^{58}, Ni^{58}(n,2n)Ni^{57} and Ni^{58}(n,np)Co^{57}, cross sections at 14.1-m.e.v. Rept. ANU/P200 Australian National University.

Rao, M.V.K.A., S. Biswas, R.R.Daniel, K.A. Neelakantan, and B. Peters. 1958. Abundance of Light Nuclei in the Primary Cosmic Radiation. Phys. Rev. 110, 751.

Rudstam, G., 1956. PhD. thesis, Uppsala.

Rudstam, G., P.C. Stevenson, and R.L.Folger. 1952 Nuclear Reactions of Iron with 340-Mev. Protons. Phys. Rev. 87, 358.

Schaeffer, O.A. and J. Zahringer. 1958. He and Ar production in Fe targets by high energy protons. Z. Naturforsch. 13a, 346.

Schaeffer, O.A., and J. Zahringer. 1959. High-Sensitivity Mass Spectrometric measurement of Stable Helium and Argon Isotopes Produced by High-Energy Protons in Iron. Phys. Rev. 113, 679.

Schaeffer, O.A., and J. Zahringer. 1960. Helium, Neon and Argon isotopes in some iron meteorites. Geochim. et Cosmochim. Acta, 19, 44.

Shapiro, M.M., B. Stiller, M. Birnbaum, and F. W. O'Dell. 1951. Transition Effect in Pb of the Star-Producing Radiation in the Stratosphere. I. Phys. Rev. 83. 455.

Sharp, R.A., R.M. Diamond, and G. Wilkinson. 1956. Nuclear Reactions of Cobalt with Protons from 0^- to 100^- Mev Energy. Phys. Rev. 101,1493.

Shedlovsky, J.P. 1960. PhD. thesis, Princeton University.

Signer, P. and A.O. Nier. 1960. The distribution of cosmic-ray produced rare gases in iron meteorites, J. Geophys. Research, 65, 2947.

Soberman, R.K. 1956. High-Altitude Cosmic-Ray Neutron Intensity Variations. Phys. Rev.101, 1399.

Sprague, A.D., D.M. Haskin, R.G. Glasser, and M. Schein. 1959. Analysis of 405-Mev. Proton and 222-Mev Negative Pion Stars. Phys. Rev.94,994.

Sprenkel, E. 1959. PhD. thesis, University of Rochester.

Stauffer, H., M. Honda. 1961. J. Geophysical

Research, in press.

Stoenner, R.W., O.A. Stauffer, and R. Davis,Jr. 1960. AEC Rept. BNL-4862.

Sugihara, T.T., and W.F. Libby. 1952. Negative Pion Activation of Bromine. Phys. Rev. 88, 587.

Van Allen, J.A., and L.A. Frank. 1959. Nature, 184, 219.

Van Dilla, M.A., J.R. Arnold, and E.C. Anderson. 1960. Spectrometric measurement of natural and cosmic-ray induced radioactivity in meteorites. Geochim. et Cosmochim. Acta, 20, 115.

Vernov, S.N., and A. Ye. Chudakev. 1959. (translated in Soviet Phys. Doklady, 4, 338.)

Vilcsek, E., and H. Wanke. 1961. Na^{22} in the Buclscheid meteorite. Z. Naturforschung, 16a, 379.

Voshage, H., and H. Hintenberger. 1959. Potassium isotopes as reaction products of cosmic radiation in the Fe meteorite Carbo. Z. Naturforschung. 14a, 828.

Wanke, H. 1960. Sc^{45} als Reaktionsprodukte der Hohenstrahlung in Meteoriten, II, Z. Naturforschung, 15a, 953.

Winsberg, L. 1954. Interaction of Negative Pions with Iodine. Phys. Rev. 95, 198.

PARMATMA S. GOEL

Tata Institute of Fundamental Research

TRUMAN P. KOHMAN

Carnegie Institute of Technology

Carbon-14 in a Stone and an Iron

Cosmic-ray-produced carbon-14 is expected to be present in most meteorites. We have detected and measured this nuclide in the chondrite Richardton and the iron meteorite Henbury. The results are consistent with expectations based on an approximately constant cosmic-ray intensity.

Experimental

To extract carbon from chondrite, a sample of about 10 g is crushed, mixed with 50 g of a mixture of lead and potassium chromates (10:1) and fused in a porcelain crucible at about 1000°C for four hours under oxygen at a pressure of about 10 cm. The gases are passed through a heated quartz tube packed with layers of CuO (700°C) and silver wool (400°C). Moisture is removed by a dry ice-acetone trap, the CO_2 is condensed in a liquid N_2 trap, and other gases are pumped off. The CO_2 is then passed through a hot tube packed with layers of platinized asbestos and silver wool; the former oxidizes any SO_2 to SO_3, which is held by the latter. Carbon dioxide is condensed in a liquid N_2 trap, and any non-condensable gases are pumped away.

The decomposition of meteoritic iron is carried out in a closed Pyrex system by slow addition of 8 $\underline{M}$ nitric acid. The solution is continuously swept with well purified air and re-

1. COSMIC-RAY-INDUCED RADIOACTIVITIES IN METEORITES - IV

fluxed for about 20 hours. If graphitic carbon
is present in the meteorite it remains essentially undecomposed, but our specimen of Henbury was
found to be free from graphite. The outgoing
gases are passed through an absorption tower
(T-1) containing carbonate-free NaOH solution,
bubbled through $KMnO_4$ solution, passed over hot
CuO, and passed through two more NaOH towers
(T-2 and T-3). T-1 served primarily to neutral-
ize acid vapours; the carbon, which is now con-
verted to CO_2, is absorbed mainly in T-2 and
T-3. The carbonate is precipitated as $BaCO_3$,
liberated again by dilute sulphuric acid, absorbed in NaOH solution and reprecipitated as
$BaCO_3$. The chemical yield at this point is
taken as $(80 \pm 5)\%$ from runs made on several
steel alloys of known carbon content, in which
the yields varied between 73 and 85%.

For purification, the CO_2 (generated from the
$BaCO_3$ with concentrated H_2SO_4 in the vacuum
system in the case of irons) is passed through
a hot tube packed with Ag-CuO-Cu-CuO-Ag layers
and condensed with liquid N_2, and non-condensable gases are pumped off. At this point the
CO_2 samples often showed some alpha activity,
presumably radon. Accordingly all samples are
further purified by absorption in 1 N NaOH solution, regeneration with concentrated H_2SO_4, passage through the Ag-CuO-Cu-CuO-Ag train, and
pumping while trapped with liquid N_2. One such
repurification has always proved sufficient.

The volume of the sample is then measured before introduction into the counter. The chemical yield was essentially quantitative in a run
on a granite-SiC mixture. The over-all yield is
accordingly taken to be $(95 \pm 3)\%$ for stones and
$(80 \pm 5)\%$ for irons.

Counters were made after the design of Stoenner et al. (1960). The CO_2 is filled by conden-
sation in a cold finger on the jacket of the
counter. The pure CO_2 alone serves as the counting gas in the proportional region. The counter
is operated in a sheath of anti-coincidence
Geiger counters within a massive shield of mer-
cury and steel. The counting circuitry provides

for separate recording of the small pulses produced by the C^{14} betas and of larger pulses produced mainly by alpha particles. The counting
yields of the counters were determined with a
standard source of C^{14} obtained from the National Bureau of Standards.

Results

The results of the measurements together with
some relevant information on the counters are giv-
en in Table 1. The Henbury carbon specific activity is about the same as that of contemporary
terrestrial carbon, so that we are unable to
exclude the possibility that part or all of this
C^{14} is a result of contamination by non-meteorit-
ic carbon, as by leakage of atmospheric CO_2 into
the gas system. The Richardton carbon specific
activity, however, is definitely too high to
admit of the latter explanation.

Discussion

Our Richardton sample contains 62 dis min^{-1}
kg^{-1} of Al^{26} (Ehmann and Kohman, 1958), giving
a C^{14}/Al^{26} activity ratio of 1.26. The production of C^{14} occurs mainly from oxygen via the
reactions $O^{16}(p,3p)C^{14}$ and $O^{16}(n,2pn)C^{14}$ and
that of Al^{26} from silicon via $Si^{26}(p,2pn)Al^{26}$
and $Si^{26}(n,p2n)Al^{26}$. In this meteorite the
ratio of the target atoms O/Si is about 3.4
(Quirke, 1919), and is not likely to vary significantly as indicated by the chemical analyses
of different chondrites (Wiik, 1956). We would
expect the C^{14}/Al^{26} production-rate ratio to be
less than the O/Si ratio for several reasons:
(i) the ratio of the geometrical cross section
of O^{16} to Si^{26} is 0.7; (ii) a $(p,3p)$ process has
fewer reaction paths than a $(p,2pn)$ process;
(iii) more protons must cross the barrier in the
former case. An opposing factor, the higher
barrier for $Z \sim 14$ than for $Z \sim 8$, could hardly be
as important as the first three. The observed
C^{14} activity corresponds roughly with expectations on the assumption that the cosmic radiation has been essentially constant for the past
million years or so.

The Henbury sample has 2.5 dis $min^{-1}kg^{-1}$ of

Table 1.   Data on the samples and counters

Meteorite	Richardton (Chondrite)	Henbury (Iron)
Specimen weight (g)	14.6	287
Total carbon content (mg)	12.6	21.2
Weight fraction of carbon (%)	0.086	0.0074
Fraction of CO_2 in counter	0.84	0.66
Total volume of counter (cm^3)	23.1	35.2
Sensitive volume of counter (cm^3)	16.8	27.6
Pressure of filling (cm Hg)	71.4	62
Background rate (cpm)	0.27 ± 0.02	0.42 ± 0.02
Sample rate above background (cpm)	0.47 ± 0.04	0.12 ± 0.03
Counting yield	0.49	0.51
Carbon specific activity (dis $min^{-1} g^{-1}$)	90 ± 8	16 ± 4
Specimen specific activity (dis $min^{-1} kg^{-1}$)	78 ± 6	1.2 ± 0.3

Be^{10} (Chakrabartty, 1961), giving a C^{14}/Be^{10} ratio of 0.6. Barr (1957) has measured the production cross sections of a large number of radionuclides from copper under 5.7-Gev proton bombardment, and extrapolated the values to C^{14} and Be^{10}; their ratio is 0.36. Since both C^{14} and Be^{10} are produced only in high-energy nuclear reactions in Fe and Ni and since our Henbury sample appeared to be fairly pure metal, the production rate ratio should be about the same in the meteorite. The fact that its observed C^{14} activity is not below the expected level for an iron in space suggests that the terrestrial age of Henbury, and hence of the associated craters (see Prior and Hey, 1953, p. 420), is not more than a few thousand years. This conclusion is only tentative, however, until the possibility of contamination of the meteoritic carbon by atmospheric carbon can be checked. Further measurements are planned.

Following establishment of the C^{14} levels and ratios to longer-lived nuclides in dated falls, measurements of C^{14} in meteoritic finds should be valuable for determining the terrestrial ages of the latter. This should be especially interesting for iron finds, many of which are 1500 years old terrestrially as indicated by the absence of the 325-year Ar^{38}(Fireman and De Felice, 1960; Wanke, 1961).

Meteoritic C^{14} measurements in connection with more refined calculations or experimental determinations of production rate ratios using accelerators should be important in detecting possible variations in the cosmic radiation intensity in the last 10^4 years. The possibility of such variations is suggested by the presumed importance of supernovae as sources of much of the cosmic radiation, so that the eruption of a nearby supernova should be followed by a "wave" of excess particles. The nuclides considered by Arnold, Honda, and Lal (1961) in arriving at the conclusion that the cosmic-ray intensity has been constant to within a factor of about two for millions of years in the past contain a wide gap in half-lives between a few hundred years

Ar^{39}, Si^{32}, Ti^{44}) and a few hundred thousand years (Cl^{36}, Al^{26}), so that variations with characteristic times of 10^4 years would not have been detected. For various reasons the approximate constancy of the biosphere C^{14} specific activity during the past few thousand years (Libby, 1955; Munnich, Ostlund, and de Vries, 1958; Ralph and Stuckenrath, 1960) are not necessarily inconsistent with a substantially higher atmospheric production rate a few thousand years earlier. Moreover, as pointed out to us by Dr. Julian Shedlovsky, "young" cosmic radiation from a nearby supernova might consist mainly of relatively low-energy particles which might be prevented by the earth's magnetic field from reaching the atmosphere and producing C^{14} therein, but which could still induce C^{14} in meteorites, especially near the surfaces of stones. Thus depth dependence studies of C^{14} should be particularly important.

These measurements, particularly of stones, are continuing.

Acknowledgements

We thank Mr. Franc Mesojedec for assistance with the electronic equipment and Dr. R. Davis, Jr., for advice on the construction of low level counters. The Henbury sample was generously provided by Dr. Brian Mason. This work was supported by the U. S. Atomic Energy Commission.

REFERENCES

Arnold, J. R., Honda, M., and Lal, D. (1961) The record of cosmic ray intensity in the meteorites. Manuscript.

Barr, D. W. (1957) Nuclear Reactions of copper induced by 5.7 Bev protons. Thesis, UCRL 3793.

Chakrabartty, M. M. (1961) Unpublished results in this laboratory.

Ehmann, W. D. and Kohman, T. P. (1958) Cosmic-ray-induced radioactivities in meteorites. II: Al^{26}, Be^{10} and Co^{60} in aerolites, siderites and tektites. Geochim. et Cosmochim. Acta 14,364.

Fireman, E. L. and De Felice, J. (1960) Argon-39

and tritium in meteorites. Geochim. et Cosmo-chim. Acta 18, 183.

Libby, W. F. (1955) Radiocarbon Dating, 2nd Ed. University of Chicago Press, Chicago, Illinois.

Munnich, K. O., Ostlund, H. G., and de Vries, H. L. (1958) Carbon-14 activity during last 5,000 years. Nature 182, 1432.

Prior, J. T. and Hey, M. H. (1953) Catalog of Meteorites, 2nd Ed. The British Museum, London.

Quirke, T. T. (1919) The Richardton meteorite. J. Geol. 27, 431.

Ralph, E. K. and Stuckenrath, R. (1960) Carbon-14 measurements of known age samples. Nature 188, 185.

Stoenner, R. W., Schaeffer, O. A., and Davis, R. (1960) Meteorites as space probes for testing the spatial constancy of cosmic radiation. J. Geophys. Res. 65, 3025.

Wanke, H. (1961) Private communication of work at Mainz.

Wiik, H. B. (1955) The chemical composition of some stony meteorites. Geochim. et Cosmochim. Acta 9, 279.

T. B. MASSALSKI

Mellon Institute

Some Metallurgical Aspects

in the Study of Meteorites

One of the main aspects in the study of meteorites is the discussion and the evaluation of the processes that may have produced the samples available on the earth. It is generally agreed that the majority of such samples are fragments of larger bodies which became broken up. Therefore, of particular interest is the size of the original bodies. From this point of view the theories concerning the origin of meteorites may be conveniently divided into three groups, each distinguished by the dimensions and by the "history" suggested for the original parent bodies. (Anders and Goles, 1961) The first such group includes objects of planetary size, intermediate between the size of the moon and that of the earth. (Ringwood, 1959; Lovering, 1957; 1958; Uhlig, 1954) In the second may be included theories which postulate that primary objects of lunar size were followed by secondary objects of asteroidal size, (Urey, 1956; 1957; 1958) and in the third group, theories which consider objects of asteroidal size only, ranging from extremely small fragments to bodies of about 200-250 km in radius. (Anders and Goles, 1961; Fish, Goles and Anders, 1960)

Each range of sizes imposes certain require-

ments upon the conditions which must have existed during the initial formation of the meteorites and during their subsequent thermal, chemical and mechanical history. Associated with the
size of the parent bodies are, for example, such
features as the time of cooling, the nature of
the Widmanstatten pattern, the chemical equilibrium, the pressure, the energy released during
collisions and many others. Although the totally metallic meteorites (the irons) are relatively rare, such meteorites are sometimes better
preserved than the stony meteorites because of
their resistance to corrosion, impact and chemical action prior and subsequent to their falling
upon the earth. The record in the irons is,
therefore, of particular interest.

Since the discovery of the Widmanstatten pattern the metallic meteorites have been studied
in detail. In such studies metallurgical observations and interpretations can be of much help,
and the number of papers which involve metallurgical discussion has grown to be quite large.
It may perhaps be advisable for the purpose of
this symposium to review briefly the particular
metallurgical observations available, and the
possible information which they may or may not
reveal. In Table I an attempt is made to tabu-
late the possible events in meteoritic history
and their metallurgical interpretation. This
tabulation is arbitrary and no claim is made to
completeness. The subsequent discussion deals
mainly with some aspects concerning the division
of the irons into hexahedrites, octahedrites and
ataxites, some features of the Widmanstatten pattern and the subdivision of octahedrites.

The Division of the Irons and the Widmanstatten
Pattern

The division of iron meteorites into hexahedrites, octahedrites and ataxites has been discussed recently by Perry (1944) and by Uhlig.
(1954). According to Uhlig no octahedrites
should be observed in meteorites whose nickel
content exceeds about 13%. This follows from a
suggestion that the majority of iron meteorites

TABLE I

Process, Event or Conditions	Accompanying Features	Possible Metallurgical Evidence and Some Selected Reference to Particular Observations
Original condensation of nebulae. Melting of interior, possible pools of metal. Sizes and numbers of original bodies. Melting and solidification of original bodies.	Temperature, Time, Pressure, Diffusion. Characteristic or abrupt changes in composition. Size of molten core. Interaction between metallic and non-metallic constituents. Volcanic-like eruptions. Passages of hot gases. Breakup of crust. Occasional rapid cooling.	Nature and size of principle metallic phases.[1-5] Crystallographic relationships.[5-11] Differences in chem. comp. and comp. gradients.[12-16] Nature and details of Widmanstatten patterns.[1,2,5,9,12,17-21] Evidence for pressure or absence of pressure.[2,22-25] Evidence for the time taken during cooling.[2,19,23,24,26,27] Details of solidification.[24] Details of equilibrium and non-equilibrium conditions.[1,2,5,14-16] Nature of impurities and their structure and morphology.[1,5] Details of kamacite, taenite and plessite.[1,5,6] Presence of martensite.[1,2,22] Recrystallization.[1,22] Presence of diamonds.[3,4,22,23] Sulphur and phosphorus distribution.[24,25] Distribution of trace impurities.[1,2,13,30] Microhardness changes.[2,31-33]
Breakup of original bodies. Mechanical Disturbances. Collisions and shock waves.	Plastic deformation. Fracture Pulverization. Partial heating. Slow or rapid cooling.	Slip bands, twinning (Neumann bands).[6] fracture bending.[1] local recrystallization. Partial dissolution of impurities. Breakup of brittle inclusions. Composition gradients.[13,16]
Possible agglomeration of solid or molten particles on surfaces of original bodies, or into new secondary bodies.	Sintering processes. Partial heating and partial melting. Diffusion at low temperature. Collisions.	Characteristic changes in the microstructure.[24,26,28] Composition gradients. Presence of chondrules and nature of metallic phases in chondrites and chondrules.[5,26,34]
Passage through earth's atmosphere. Impact with the earth. Corrosion and errosion following a fall.	Aerodynamic heating of the surface. Plastic deformation and shock waves. Rapid energy changes. Fracture. Oxidation and contamination.	Surface melting, heat-affected zones.[31,35] Recrystallization, deformation, twinning, slip.[34] Bending, fracture, breakup into fragments.[3,4,5] Crystallographic transformations. Hydration. Weathering of the kamacite phase.[5]

REFERENCES FOR TABLE I

1. Perry, 1944
2. Uhlig, 1954
3. Nininger, 1952
4. Nininger, 1956
5. Nininger, 1960
6. Uhlig, 1955
7. Mehl, 1938
8. Mehl and Derge, 1937
9. Buddhue, 1948
10. Owen, 1940
11. Owen and Burns, 1939
12. Nininger et al., 1957
13. Nichiporuh 1958
14. Maringer et al., 1959
15. Feller-Kniepmeyer & Uhlig, 1961
16. Yavnell et al., 1958
17. Urey, 1961
18. Brezina, 1885
19. Massalski and Park, 1961
20. Perry, 1940
21. Smith and Young, 1939
22. Lipshutz and Anders, 1961
23. Urey, 1956
24. Fish et al., 1960
25. Vogel and Neumann, 1946
26. Urey and Mayeda, 1959
27. Allen and Jacobs, 1936
28. Anders and Goles, 1961
29. Vogel, 1951
30. Goldberg et al., 1951
31. Maringer et al., 1958
32. Dalton, 1950
33. Dalton, 1951
34. Sorby, 1877
35. Opik, 1958

cooled under conditions of large pressure (-10^5 atm.) in a single parent body of planetary size and that this pressure displaced the onset of the precipitation of the kamacite phase to much lower temperatures.

Nevertheless, the presence or absence of the Widmanstatten pattern may be a somewhat doubtful criterion to determine the magnitude of the pressure since it is governed by a number of factors not all of which are yet understood. Examination of Figure 1 in which 114 iron meteorites have been plotted against their nickel content shows, for example, that octahedrites exist whose overall Ni composition exceeds 13% and that there seems to be no definite cut-off composition for the occurrence of the octahedral pattern.* One would in general expect the octahedrite pattern to be fine in meteorites of high nickel content because the initial nucleation would then have occurred at relatively low temperatures (between 650-500°C) at which diffusion rates are low. Each individual kamacite band would grow only to a limited extent leading to a <u>fine</u> pattern. In addition, the frequency of nucleation may have been high at such temperatures, particularly if some supercooling existed. While pressure may have contributed to some particular features of the Widmanstatten pattern, including its dimensions, the presence or absence of this pattern cannot be a function of composition or pressure alone. For example, the crystallographic habit planes on which precipitation of one phase occurs within another phase are usually a function of the temperature and become complex and more numerous with the fall of temperature because they

---

* It is of interest to note that the distribution shown in Figure 1 indicates a few abrupt steps in an otherwise smooth curve. The occurrence of these steps may be coincidental, but it may be associated, at least in part, with the differences between the origin or sizes of the parent bodies. Similar unexplained differences are found, for example, in the contents of certain trace impurities. (Lovering et al, 1957).

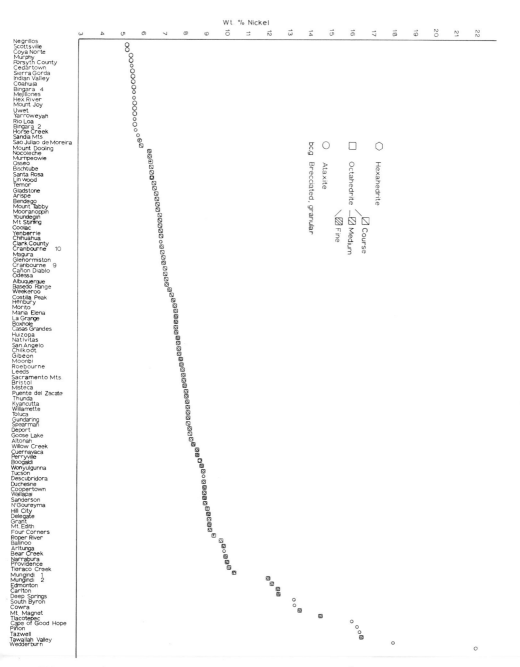

Figure 1: The designated names of 114 metallic meteorites plotted in terms of their total nickel content.

are affected by the balance between the surface
energy (important at high temperatures) and the
strain energy (important at low temperatures).
The frequent absence of a macroscopic-scale
Widmanstatten pattern in nickel-rich irons
(nickel content $>10\%$) may be, in part, associated with such a change in the crystallographic
habit of the precipitate.

The following general factors associated with
the formation of the Widmanstatten pattern may
be considered of particular interest, all of
which are a function of the nature and the size
of the parent body: i) the time of segregation;
ii) the initial and final temperature of segregation; iii) the pressure; iv) the impurities;
and v) the chemical composition of the kamacite
and taenite phases.

The time taken for the segregation of the
Widmanstatten pattern can be in principle related to the total lifetime of the meteoritic bodies.
It has been suggested (Uhlig, 1954) that the dimensions of the bands in a Widmanstatten pattern,
and its general coarseness, indicate very long
segregation times. To a certain extent this
depends on the general model which is assumed to
depict the process of Widmanstatten precipitation. For the majority of the octahedrites it
appears justifiable to assume that the Widmanstatten pattern formed as a result of slow cooling from the taenite phase. At temperatures
above approximately 500°C the rates of diffusion
are sufficiently high to permit equilibrium
precipitation relatively quickly, at most within
a few days. This has been demonstrated by laboratory experiments. It seems likely that the
major portion of the Widmanstatten precipitation
in each meteorite could have originated under
such conditions. The size of the original taenite crystals (as indicated, for example, by
the size of the meteorite Boguslavka (Krinov,
1960)) suggests that the time available for the
growth of such large crystals was indeed very
long, perhaps amounting to thousands or millions
of years. However, it has been calculated that,
even if the size of the original asteroidal bo-

dies exceeded 200 km in radius, the total time taken for the segregation of the coarse features of the Widmanstatten pattern (under conditions of equilibrium and without large pressure) need not have exceeded about 10^7 years. (Massalski and Park)

It is possible to assume that large pressures prevented the onset of the kamacite-phase precipitation at high temperatures and that the segregation occurred mainly at temperatures below -400° or 350°C. In such cases an enormously long time would be required for the segregation of the patterns observed in the meteoritic samples (Uhlig, 1954; Urey, 1956). Fish, Goles and Anders (1960) and Lipschutz and Anders (1961) have suggested recently that the size of the asteroidal bodies need not have exceeded about 200 km in radius with a corresponding pressure of about 600 atmospheres. The effect of such pressures on the Widmanstatten pattern cannot be, at the moment, assessed adequately; but it should be intermediate between the proposal of Uhlig and precipitation without pressure.

The lowest temperature at which equilibrium conditions still existed in octahedrite meteorites upon slow cooling can be approximately evaluated in two ways: i) from the individual compositions of the kamacite and taenite phases and from the composition of plessite; and ii) from the ratio of the kamacite/taenite phases. Following recent measurements of the composition gradients of Ni in octahedrite meteorites by the electron-probe microbeam methods, (Maringer et al, 1959; Feller-Kniepmeyer and Uhlig, 1961; Yavnell et al, 1958) it has been established that the composition of the α phase corresponds to low Ni contents and therefore to low temperatures of final equilibration, while the composition of the taenite phase corresponds to higher temperatures (see Table 2). The interface between the kamacite and taenite phases is rich in Ni on the taenite side (-30% Ni or more) and contains about 6-7.5% Ni on the kamacite side. Such a difference of composition cannot be satisfactorily interpreted in terms of a single

Table II

Meteorite	MICROBEAM ANALYSES							CHEMICAL ANALYSES	
	Ni Content and the Corresponding Temp, in °C*						Reference	Gross Ni Content	Reference
	Kamacite		Taenite		Plessite				
Grant	6.61%	~403	35-85%	~?	14.8%	~638	Maringer et al., 1959	9.35%	Henderson, 1941
	6.6%	~403	23-32.4%	~472	13-19%	~659	Feller-Kniepmeier & H. H. Uhlig, 1961		
Cañon Diablo	7.0%	~367	31-34%	~462	16-20%	~624	"	7.1%	Goldberg et al., 1951
Glorieta Mountain	7.5%	~329	26-32.5%	~473	15%	~635	"	11.79%	Henderson, 1941
Dexter	6.8%	~383	52.3%	~335	14.5%	~641	"	7.9%	Uhlig, 1954, 1955
El Capitan	7.0%	~369	30%	~491	11.5-16%	~678	"	8.4%	Howell, 1895
Casas Grandes	6.0%	~450	30%	~491	11.5%	~678	"	7.73%	Cohen, 1892
Xiquipilco (Toluca)	7.5%	~329	30-42%	~405	15%	~635	"	8.25%	Nichiporuk, 1958
Chebankol	7.6-6.4%	~323	32-42%	~405	20%	~582	Yavnel et al., 1958	9.03%	Yavnel et al., 1958

*Where possible the lowest nickel content in kamacite, the highest nickel content in taenite on the α/γ interface and the lowest nickel content in plessite was used

114

equilibrium temperature. Assuming that plessite
formed inside the taenite grains when long diffusion paths were no longer possible* the composition of the plessitic areas should be indicative of the lowest temperature at which equilibrium conditions existed throughout the Widmanstatten pattern. In many octahedrite meteorites this composition amounts to about 15-
16% of Ni and corresponds to a temperature of
about 630°C. The general conclusion, therefore,
is that long-range diffusion began to break
down in the taenite phase in the vicinity of
600°C but was maintained within the kamacite
phase at very much lower temperatures. As measured in meteoritic samples the final composition
of the taenite and kamacite phases do not correspond, therefore, to any single temperature.

However, a measure of the lowest temperature
at which equilibrium conditions existed can be
estimated from the ratio of the kamacite-taenite
phases based upon quantitative metallographic
measurements on a polished surface of a meteorite (Massalski and Park). Such studies in five
typical octahedrites indicate that the final
temperature of equilibrium lies between 430° and
530°C. Below these temperatures additional precipitation of the kamacite occurred only under
conditions of localized diffusion. The metallographic study also shows that the five meteorites
could be divided into two groups according to
the final temperature of equilibration. This
may indicate that they originated in at least
two different parent bodies. (Massalski and
Park, 1961).

Relatively little is known about the influence

---

*Uhlig (1955) suggests that plessite could have
originated in two different ways: by precipitation of kamacite from the taenite phase at low
temperatures and by a martensitic transformation
of the taenite phase following a sudden change
in the pressure. It is of interest to note that
these two different modes of formation should
result in a different habit plane and could be
studied by X-ray techniques.

of impurities with regard to the nature, coarseness, and the time taken for the growth of the
Widmanstatten pattern. Vogel (1951) and Du-
Fresne and Anders (1961) have suggested that influence of phosphorus may be of particular importance. According to the Fe-P phase diagram
(Hansen and Anderko, 1958) the presence of
phosphorus in the amounts of a fraction of a
percent profoundly influences the general phase
equilibria. For example, if the amount of phosphorus exceeds about 0.2%, the kamacite phase
displaces the taenite phase at high temperatures
thus removing the basis for the formation of a
Widmanstatten pattern. In a similar way, the
influence of cobalt (the usual content of Co in
Fe meteorites is of the order of about 0.5%),
and of sulfur should also be considered.

Finally, it is of interest to note that the
taenite phase containing less than 25% Ni cannot
be retained at room temperature (Hansen and Anderko, 1958). On cooling, it always transforms
martensitically into a body-centered structure.
There is evidence that in some meteorites the
final microstructure has indeed been produced
as a result of a martensitic transformation,
(Perry, 1944) but on the whole the presence of
a coarse Widmanstatten pattern along simple
crystallographic habit planes strongly suggest
that precipitation occurred under conditions of
very slow cooling controlled by diffusion.

Classification of Octahedrites

The system of classification of octahedrites
according to kamacite band-width was defined by
Brezina (1885) who divided octahedrites into
five different groups. Recently, Lovering et
al. (1957) have suggested that a division of
octahedrites into only three groups represents
a more natural division. The difference between
the Brezina and the Lovering et al. classification contrasted with the occurrence of 63 octahedrites studied by Lovering et al. is shown in
Figure 2. Such classifications are of interest,
but they appear to be unsatisfactory if they are
to be used as a basis for studying the differ-

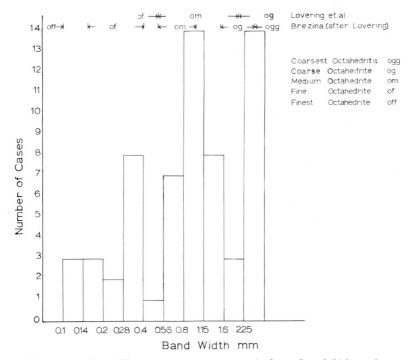

Figure 2: The mean apparent band-width of 63 octahedrites super-imposed upon the proposed octahedrite classifications of Brezina (1885) and Lovering et al. (1957)

ences between octahedrites. It can be seen, for example, that the distribution of the mean apparent band widths in the 63 samples follows a complex pattern in which several peaks can be distinguished. Yet, there seems to be no a priori reason why the distribution of octahedrites should show peaks at certain values of bandwidths, unless this is in some way connected with the particular set of samples which were studied, or the origin of the bodies from which these meteorites came. As has been pointed out by Lovering et al. (1957) any obtained distribution also depends upon the geometrical relationships between the plane of section of each investigated sample and the actual orientation of the kamacite band within the sample. The measurement of the kamacite band-width may yield different results depending on whether the plane of the examined section is parallel to the cubic, octahedral or hexahedral planes of the original taenite crystal.

Examination of Figure 1 shows that in some cases the fineness of the octahedrite pattern appears to be out of line with the measured chemical composition. A likely reason for this is that, in addition to the influence of composition, the time available for the formation of the Widmanstatten pattern, and the pressure under which this pattern was produced, also play a role. For example, a fine octahedrite might be obtained in a meteorite of high Ni content when cooled extremely slowly and without pressure. Both the pressure and the rate of cooling are related to the size of the original parent body, and hence the nature of the octahedrite pattern is closely related to the theories of meteorite formation.

An alternative method of designating octahedrites might perhaps be desirably based upon the total content of the kamacite phase with respect to the taenite phase. In the majority of cases the present classification in terms of the band widths should be a function of the total content of the kamacite phase in a sample. A quantitative ratio of the kamacite/taenite phases can be obtained from a polished section of a meteoritic sample and the result should not be particularly dependent upon the crystallographic relationships between the kamacite and taenite phases or the details of equilibrium.

ACKNOWLEDGMENTS

It is a pleasure to acknowledge stimulating discussions with Dr. H.W. King and Mr. F.R. Park. This work has been supported in part by a research grant from the National Aeronautics and Space Administration, Washington 25, D.C.

REFERENCES

Allan, D.W. and J.A. Jacobs. 1936. The melting of asteroids and the origin of meteorites, Geochim. et Cosmochim, Acta, 9, 256

Anders, E. and G.G. Goles. 1961. Theories on the Origin of Meteorites, Journ. of Chem. Ed., 38, 58.

Brezina, A. 1885. Die Meteoritensammlung des mineralogischen Hofcabinetes in Wien am 1 Mai 1885, Jahrb. K.K. Geological Reichsanstadt, 35, 151.

Buddhue, J.D. 1948. Synthetic metallic meteorites, Pop.Astron., 56, 105.

Cohen, E. 1892. Meteoreisen-Studien II, Ann. K. K. Naturhist. Hofmus, Wien, I, 157.

Dalton, F.K. 1950. Microhardness testing of iron meteorites, J. Roy. Astron. Soc. Can., 44,185.

Dalton, F.K. 1951. Microhardness testing of iron meteorites, J. Roy. Astron. Soc. Can., 45,162.

DuFresne, E.R. 1961. unpublished work quoted in Fish et al., 1960.

Feller-Kniepmeyer, M. and H.H.Uhlig. 1961. Nickel analyses of metallic meteorites by the electron probe microanalyser, Geochim et Cosmochim, Acta, 21, 257.

Fish, R.A., G.G. Goles and E. Anders. 1960. The Record in the Meteorites. III. On the Development of Meteorites in Asteroidal Bodies. Astrophys. Journal, 132, 243.

Goldberg, E., A. Uchiyama and H. Brown. 1951. The Distribution of nickel, cobalt, gallium, pallodium and gold in iron meteorites, Geochim. et Cosmochim. Acta, 2, 1.

Hansen, M. and K. Anderko. 1958. Constitution of Binary Alloys, McGraw-Hill, New York.

Henderson, E.P. 1941. Corrections to Published Analyses of Meteorites, Amer. J. Sci., 239, 407.

Howell, E.E. 1895. On two new meteorites, Amer. J. Sci., 50, 253.

Krinov, E.L. 1960. Principles of Meteorites (Translation), Pergamon Press, New York.

Lipshutz, M.E. and E. Anders. 1961. The Record in the meteorites -IV. Origin of diamonds in iron meteorites, Geochim. et Cosmochim. Acta, 24, 83.

Lovering, J.F. 1957. Pressures and temperatures within a typical parent meteorite body, Geochim. et. Cosmochim. Acta, 12, 253.

Lovering, J.F. 1958. A typical parent meteorite body, Geochim. et Cosmochim. Acta, 14, 174.

Lovering, J.F., W. Nichiporuk, A Chodos and H. Brown. 1957. Distribution of gallium, germanium, cobalt, chromium and copper in iron and stony-iron meteorites in relation to nickel content and structure, Geochim. et Cosmochim. Acta, 11, 263.

Maringes, R.E., C. R. Simcoe, G. K. Manning and L. R. Jackson. 1958. Aerodynamic heating of iron meteorites during entry into the atmosphere, Battelle Memorial Institute, Columbus, Ohio.

Maringer, R.E., N.A. Richard and A.E. Austin. 1959. Microbeam analysis of Widmanstatten structure in meteoritic iron, Trans. A.I.M.E., 215, 56.

Massalshi, T.B. and F. Park. 1961. to be published.

Mehl, R.F. and G. Deige. 1937. Widmanstatten structure (VIII) γ-α transformation in iron-nickel alloys. Trans. A.I.M.E., 125, 482.

Mehl, R.F. 1938. Iron from Heaven, Carnegie Magazine, 11, January.

Nichiporuk, W. 1958. Variations in the content of nickel, gallium, germanium, cobalt, copper and chromium in the Kamacite and taenite phases of iron meteorites, Geochim. et Cosmochim. Acta, 13, 233.

Nininger, H.H. 1952. Out of the Sky, Dover Publications, New York.

Nininger, H.H. 1956. Arizona's Meteorite Crater, American Meteorite Museum, Sedona, Arizona.

Opik, E.J. 1958. Physics of meteor flight in the atmosphere, Interscience Tracts in Physics and Astronomy, Volume 6.

Owen, E.A. 1940. The Structure of Meteoritic Iron, Phil. Mag. 29, 553.

Owen, E.A. and B. Burns. 1939. X-ray study of meteoritic irons, Phil. Mag., 28, 497.

Panith, F.A. 1940. The Origin of Meteorites,

Halley Lecture, Clarendon Press, Oxford.

Perry, S.H. 1944. The Metallography of Meteoritic Iron. U.S.National Museum Bulletin, 184.

Ringwood, A.E. 1959. Chemical Evolution and Densities of the Planets, Geochim. et Cosmochim. Acta, 15, 257.

Smith, S.W.J. and J. Young. 1939. The Widmanstatten structure of octahedral meteoritic iron, Nature, 143, 384.

Sorby, H.C. 1877. On the Structure and Origin of Meteorites, Nature, 15, 495.

Uhlig, H.H. 1954. Contribution of metallurgy to the origin of meteorites. Part I - Structure of metallic meteorites, their composition and the effect of pressure, Geochim. et Cosmochim. Acta, 6, 282.

Uhlig, H.H. 1955. Contribution of metallurgy to the origin of meteorites. Part II - The significance of Neumann bands in meteorites, Geochim. et Cosmochim. Acta, 7, 34.

Urey, H.C. 1956. Diamonds, Meteorites, and the Origin of the Solar System, Astrophys. J., 124, 623.

Urey, H.C. 1957. 41st Guthrie Lecture, Yearbook of the Physical Society, 14, London.

Urey, H.C. 1958. The early history of the solar system as indicated by the meteorites. Proc. Chem. Soc. 67, 67.

Urey, H.C. 1961. The Planets, to be published; as quoted in G.G.Goles and E.Anders, 1961.

Urey, H.C. and T. Mayeda. 1959. Metallic Particles of Chondrites, Geochim et Cosmochim Acta, 17, 113.

Urey, H.C., A. Mele and T. Mayeda. 1957. Diamonds in stone meteorites, Geochim. et Cosmochim. Acta. 13, 1.

Vogel, R. 1951. Die Gefuge formen des Meteoreisens und ihre Erklarung auf Grund des Zustandsdiagrammes des Systems Eisen-Nickel-Phosphor, Neues. Jahrb. Mineral Abh., 83, 23.

Vogel, R. and T. Heumann. 1946. Uber die Bildungssmoglichkeiten der Widmanstatten Struktur des meteorischen Eisens unter hohem Druck, Nachrichten der Akad. der Wissenschaften Gottingen, Math. Phys. Klasse, Heft 2, 123.

Yavnell, A.A., I. B. Borovski, N. P. Ilin and
I. D. Marchukowa. 1958. Doklady Akademii Nauk
SSSR, 123, 256.

R. E. MARINGER

G. K. MANNING

Battelle Memorial Institute

Some Observations on

Deformation and Thermal Alterations

in Meteoritic Iron

Meteoritic iron displays a rather remarkable variety of structures which are the direct result of the various events which occurred during the history of the particular fragment in question. Many of these structures are so completely different from those observed in man-made alloys that usually a metallographically polished and etched meteoritic iron can be recognized on sight. This has quite naturally led to a system of classification which involves the presence or absence of the most predominant metallographic feature, the Widmanstatten pattern. However, there is much more to the structure of meteoritic iron than such gross features, and it is becoming increasingly clear that, by understanding the nature of the fine structure, we can reconstruct a significant portion of the history of the fragments under study. As these data accumulate, we should be able to build a picture of many of the events which occurred during the formative period of our solar system.

It is possible, for example, to describe qualitatively a sequence of events to which a particular metallic meteorite has been exposed by a comparatively casual study of its metallographic features. Most irons have experienced, in the order given, the following conditions.

(1) Exposure to temperatures above or near the melting point.

> This is required to explain the very large austenitic grain size and the large inclusion size.

(2) Very slow cooling.

> This is required to explain the width of the Widmanstatten platelets and the large size of precipitated phases.

(3) Severe deformation at moderate or low temperatures.

> This is required to explain the heavy deformation twinning (Neumann lamellae) and some coarser deformation phenomena.

While this information is helpful, a number of questions immediately arise. How long did the mass remain at the melting point? How slow was the rate of cooling? At what temperature did the deformation occur? What was the mechanism and magnitude of the force causing the observed deformation?

In addition, some meteorites show a fourth step in the above sequence. Many specimens show signs of reheating to some moderately high temperature. Again questions arise. What was the source of the reheating? What were the temperatures and times involved.

We do not yet have the full answer to any of these questions. However, enough has been learned in the last few years to demonstrate that many of these questions can be answered through the use of modern metallurgical tools and techniques. It is the purpose of this paper to illustrate by a few examples some contributions which have been made and to suggest some areas in which significant contributions probably can and will be made.

SOME EXPERIMENTAL RESULTS

Deformation in Kamacite

The alpha-iron phase (kamacite) in meteoritic iron generally shows signs of deformation. In

many cases, deformation twins (Neumann lamellae)
stand out in a clear matrix as shown in Figure 1.
In other cases, there is an additional background
on the etched surface, which we have called a
"matte" structure. This is shown in Figure 2.
Here the Neumann lamellae still stand out clearly,
but obviously some substructure exists. Recently,
using a modified Fry's reagent 15 g $CuCl_2$, 40 cc
HCl, 30 cc distilled H_2O, and 25 cc ethyl alcohol)
on an electropolished surface, it has been possible to resolve this substructure. The result
is shown in Figure 3.

100X   N77370

FIGURE 1.   Rifle, Colorado Meteorite - Ragged
            diagonal lines are Neumann Lamellae.
            Note that, except for small precipi-
            tate particles, the matrix appears
            structureless.

100X   N46115

FIGURE 2.   Grant Meteorite. The left-hand por-
             tion of the photomicrograph shows
             heavily deformed kamacite. We have
             called this a "matte" structure. The
             dark patch at the lower right is ples-
             site.

It should be noted that the fine needles lie
in three principal directions, just as do the
platelets in the Widmanstatten structure. We
believe that this structure is the result of the
passage of a shock wave of sufficient intensity
to transform the body-centered-cubic kamacite to
the more dense face-centered-cubic taenite. The
matte structure then developed when the pressure
dissipated and the taenite reverted to kamacite
by a shear transformation.
    This interpretation is consistent with present-

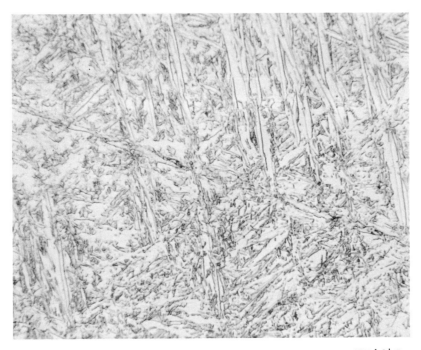

1000X   N76941

FIGURE 3.   "Matte" Structure in Kamacite of
            Grant Meteorite.
            Etched in modified Fry's reagent.

ly known facts. It has been shown, for example,
that when iron is subjected to a shock wave in
excess of 130 kilobars, a discontinuity occurs
in the Hugoniot curve, see for example McQueen
and Marsh (1960) and Smith (1958). This discontinuity is of the form of a sudden decrease in
the slope of the volume-pressure curve, suggesting that the more dense face-centered-cubic phase
has been formed. Moreover, when examined metallographically, iron specimens subjected to a
shock wave in excess of 130 kilobars develop a
substructure not unlike that observed in some meteoritic iron.
    Since the temperature of the transformation of

iron is lowered by the addition of nickel, it
seems reasonable that a shock of something less
than 130 kilobars could produce the matte structure in meteoritic iron. It would be relatively
simple to demonstrate this experimentally. If
the interpretation given above is correct, then
the existence of the matte is indicative of the
passage of a reasonably severe shock wave. It
may be possible, on closer study of this structure, to distinguish variations in the nature of
the matte which can be quantitatively related to
the severity of the shock wave. At least one such
variation appears to exist which can be seen in
microhardness data. These data will be discussed
in a later section.

C.S.Smith (1958) has shown another method of
studying the effects of shock waves on metals.
He deformed various metals by shock techniques,
then counted the number of deformation twins having a given angle with respect to some fixed direction in the specimen. He found that there
was a minimum in the number of twins whose angles
with respect to the direction of shock wave ap-
proached zero. Hence, if the sample chosen is
sufficiently large to be considered random, a
study of twin directions in kamacite should reveal the direction in which the shock wave was
traveling.

The question that naturally arises in a discussion of shock waves is "What was the source
of the shock?" There are at least three possibilities. These are:

(1) Impact with the earth
(2) Impact between asteroid particles
(3) Disruption of some larger primordial body.

In certain cases, as for example Canyon Diablo,
the impact of the meteorite with the earth was
certainly sufficiently large to produce high-
energy shock waves. Indeed, Lipschutz and Anders
(1961) have suggested that the shock was sufficiently intense to produce both the pressures and
the temperatures necessary to form the diamonds
occasionally found in Canyon Diablo specimens.
Among the smaller meteorites, those which do not
form craters, it seems quite unlikely that im-

pact with the earth could cause severe shock deformation. Experience from ballistics suggests
that a great deal of gross surface damage (perhaps similar to that seen on Amelia Farm specimens) would accompany severe impact shocks. This
would be readily observable where most or all of
the fall is recovered. Such gross surface damage
is, however, relatively rare. There is an additional argument against earth impact as a source
of shock structures. This argument is based upon the sharpness of the interface between the
recrystallized aerodynamically heated zone, and
the (visibly) unaffected metal in the interior.
This argument will be given in more detail in a
later section. We can at least tentatively conclude, then, that much of the deformation structure in meteoritic iron is extraterrestrial in
origin.

It is not easy to distinguish between the final two hypothetical sources of shock structure.
They differ, in fact, only by degree. However,
there is a possibility that a careful analysis of
the shock structure of a meteorite would reveal
the existence of secondary shocks. For example,
studies based on the nature of the aerodynamically heated zone in the Grant meteorite suggest
that an amount of material on the order of centimeters thick was lost by ablation. (Maringer and
Manning, 1960) In other words, the existing surface of the meteorite is only a few centimeters
away from the surface which existed in space.
If this specimen had been struck, in space, by a
smaller object traveling at a velocity of some
kilometers per second, one might expect to find
some clues to this secondary (?) impact, even
though the crater and much of the severe surface
damage had been lost by ablation. One might expect a gradient in the deformation structure ra-
diating away from the point of impact.

Certainly the deformation structure in kamacite
deserves more study.

Deformation in Taenite

Under certain etching conditions, it is possi-

ble to see evidence of deformation in the taenite
phase of meteoritic iron. Figure 4 gives an example of this observation. It should be noted
that the orientation of the line structures visible in Figure 4 is the same as that for the
Widmanstatten structure itself. Moreover, the
acicular structure in the plessite phase also
shares this orientation.

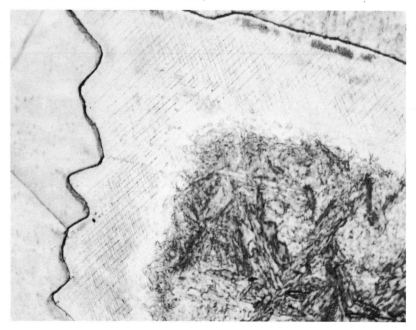

500X   N57878

FIGURE 4.   Grant Meteorite. The closely spaced
             lines are in taenite and are believed
             to represent octahedral slip. The
             dark patch at the lower right is ples-
             site. Etchant was 5g $FeCl_3$ + 50 cc
             HCl + 50 cc H_2O.

This line structure is believed to be due to
octahedral slip in the taenite. It is not clear
why these lines etch out the way they do, since
etching usually causes slip lines to disappear.

However we are inclined to believe that the high
degree of deformation within the slip traces has
caused local transformation to kamacite or
martensite.

So far as it was checked, the slip lines were
of the same orientation everywhere on the surface of the slice. This, of course, only con-
firms the conclusion that the whole meteorite
was, at some higher temperature, a single crystal
of taenite. What appears to be this same structure has also been observed in metallic particles
in the New Concord (McCall) chondrite.

Once again, lack of detailed knowledge of slip
in meteoritic gamma iron prevents the full mean-
ing of this observation being discerned. However, one possibility can be mentioned. It is
known that slip occurs on the octahedral planes
in face-centered-cubic metals. This slip is
generally localized on a series of parallel
planes. The thickness and the spacing of these
slip lines is a function of the temperature and
probably also the strain rate with the spacing
getting smaller for higher strain rates and for
lower temperatures. In Figure 4, the lines have
a spacing of about 2 microns. This is, of course,
consistent with the idea that the deformation is
the result of the passage of a shock wave. This
finding deserves closer attention since, by comparing the deformation structures in kamacite
and taenite, it is probable that a fair picture
of the nature of the forces causing these phenomena can be discerned.

Reheating of Meteoritic Iron

A number of changes occur when meteoritic iron
is reheated, most or all of which can be used to
estimate the temperatures to which the fragment
has been exposed. Evidence of reheating (at some
time since the formation of the Widmanstatten
pattern) is relatively common in meteorites.
There are several possible sources for such reheating. Some of these are:
(1) Reheating by man
(2) Aerodynamic heating during fall through

the earth's atmosphere
(3) Heating by shock waves
(4) Heating from the sun during a close orbital pass
One always has to consider the first of these when dealing with old meteorites which have been in the possession of inexperienced or primitive peoples for a number of years. However, for the most part, this possibility is easy to discount.

Aerodynamic heating, on the other hand, is common to all meteorites, although on many specimens the effects of aerodynamic heating have been lost by weathering. In other meteorites which fragmented just before or on contact with the earth, some of the surfaces will not show signs of aerodynamic heating.

There are at least three metallographically observable effects of aerodynamic heating. These are:

(1) A rather sharply defined zone of recrystallized kamacite extending some millimeters below the surface of the specimen (visible heat-affected zone).

(2) A marked gradient in the hardness of the kamacite. The heat-affected zone near the surface being perhaps 150 points Knoop softer.

(3) A lamellar structure on parts of the surface, called an ablation deposit.

An example of the visible heat-affected zone (from the Grant meteorite) is shown in Figure 5. The transition from the recrystallized zone to the visibly unaffected zone is remarkably sharp. It has been shown experimentally (Maringer and Manning, 1960) that, for times of 10 to 20 seconds at temperature, this transition occurs at about 770 C in the Grant. The temperature of this transition in the Costilla Peak, another octahedrite, is approximately the same. If one can generalize on the basis of two data points, it can be concluded that, when unrecrystallized kamacite is observed, the maximum temperature to which it has been exposed since the formation of the deformation structure must have been less than 770 C. Since recrystallization and grain growth is a function of both time and temperature, longer times at lower temperatures could also produce similar phenomena.

75X   N52096

FIGURE 5.   Visible heat-affected zone of
            Grant meteorite

The sharpness of the edge of the visible-heat-affected zone suggests that the deformation structure was in existence during the process of

ablation. In other words, the deformation structure was extraterrestrial in origin. Had the
deformation structure been the result of impact
with the earth, one would expect to observe one
of two things. If a strong thermal gradient
existed near the surface at the time of the impact, one would expect to see some changes in
the nature of the deformation near the edge of
the visible heat-affected zone. If the thermal
gradient had dissipated prior to impact, one
would expect to find evidence of shock structure
in the grains of the visible heat-affected zone.
To our knowledge, neither of these has been observed.

    Reheating of kamacite leads to a marked de-
crease in hardness. Indeed, hardness measurements were used by the authors (Maringer and Manning, 1960, 1959a, 1959b) for the major part of
a study leading to the estimation of the extent
of aerodynamic heating in the Grant and Costilla
Peak meteorites. This decrease in hardness, like
many other effects of reheating in meteoritic
iron, is both time and temperature dependent.
Some experimental data demonstrating this fact
are given in Figure 6. This decrease of hardness

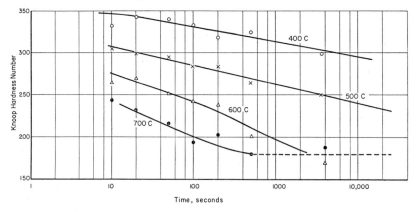

FIGURE 6.   Effect of heat-treating time on room
            temperature hardness of Grant Meteor-
            ite.

is apparently the result of the relief of internal strains, and is quite similar to the behavior of heavily cold-worked or explosively deformed iron annealed at various temperatures. The significance of these data lie in the fact that even a few hundred seconds at 400 C reveal marked softening. Hence, the Grant (except of course for the aerodynamically heated surface) must never have been exposed to temperatures above 400 C, since the formation of its deformation structure.

If, as suggested above, the deformation structure observed, the relatively high hardness, and the sensitivity of the hardness to heat treatment are all associated with the passage of a shock wave, then some general relationships between hardness and the general history of a meteorite should exist. In the Keen Mountain hexahedrite, for example, there is no matte structure, although the meteorite is heavily twinned. This might suggest that the shock which caused the twinning was considerably less than that to which the Grant and Costilla Peak had been subjected. Interestingly enough, the gradient in hardness away from the heat-affected zone in Keen Mountain was too small to be used as a temperature indicator, and our estimates of aerodynamic heating had to be based on other characteristics. In fact, the hardness of the Keen Mountain averaged out very close to the minimum hardness observed in the heat-affected zones of the Grant and Costilla Peak meteorites.

If we may again generalize on the basis of a small sample, one might expect to find that kamacite showing matte structure will usually be harder than kamacite showing no matte structure. This should be true unless some general heating has occurred since the deformation occurred. The Reed City meteorite is perhaps an extreme example of what might happen. This specimen has an easily recognizable Widmanstatten structure and a visible heat-affected zone, but has no hardness gradient and no deformation structure. The kamacite throughout the specimen is recrystallized, indicating some comparatively severe reheating prior to its entry into the atmosphere. A less

severe reheating might have considerably soften-
ed the specimen without destroying much of the
observable deformation structure. As a tool,
therefore, it appears that hardness measurements
can be useful both as an indicator of the magnitude of the shock which produced the deformation
and as an indicator of the temperatures to which
shocked material has been exposed. It would be
particularly interesting to pursue this line of
inquiry on a variety of specimens of Canyon
Diablo. It may be possible to show by hardness
and structure observations some regular variations related to shock-wave attenuation and re-
flected shockwave interactions.

Certainly, if shock waves can cause reheating,
we can expect to find meteorites which were recrystallized as the result of collisions in space.
There is even some hope of separating such specimens from those in which the recrystallization
resulted from a longer heating and cooling period,
such as might be expected from an orbital pass
close to the sun. Rapidly heated and cooled
kamacite, such as that found in the aerodynamically heat-affected zone of meteorites, has very
irregular-sized-and-shaped grains. This can be
seen in Figure 4. On the other hand, kamacite
which has recrystallized over longer times at
(very probably) much lower temperatures has a
much more uniform grain size. It is just this
fact which permits the heat-affected zone on the
(extraterrestrially) recrystallized Reed City meteorite to be so readily observable.

One final result of reheating on the metallic
phases of meteorites is so-called ablation deposit. As metal on the frontal surface of a falling meteorite is aerodynamically heated, it melts
and is subsequently swept away by the on-rushing
atmosphere, and is partially deposited on less-
exposed surfaces. This type of deposit is relatively common, (Maringer, 1960) and may be the
source of some interesting additional information.

When well formed, these deposits have a characteristic lamellar structure, as shown in Figure
7. The deposit picture is from the Costilla Peak
meteorite, and has some 12 or 14 fairly distinct

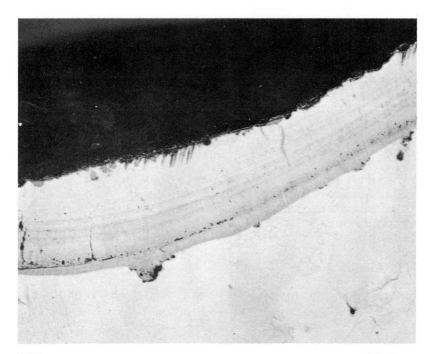

10X   N44591

FIGURE 7.   Layered "Ablation Deposit" (center)
            on rear surface of Costilla Peak
            Meteorite (bottom)

layers. There is apparently a relation between
the thickness of the layers and the sequence in
which they were laid down, for each successive
layer differs in thickness by about the same a-
mount. Presumably these layers represent successive waves of molten material swept away from
the frontal surface and deposited on the protected rear surface. Does this mean that the rate
of ablation diminished during later stages of
the fall? Does this mean that the protected
rear surface is the actual surface that existed
in space? We don't know the answer to these
questions yet, but we can suggest that a careful
study of the almost totally ignored ablation de-

posits could be very fruitful.

Effects of Reheating on Second Phases

The solid solubility of the elements carbon and phosphorus in alpha iron decreases with decreasing temperature. For carbon, the solubility in the high-temperature gamma phase is much greater than in the low-temperature alpha phase. As a result of this and the fact that meteoritic iron was cooled very slowly, most of the carbon and phosphorus present are in the form of precipitated compounds. The particles are very large compared to those found in man-made alloys. This suggests that the cooling rate was very slow compared to the rate man-made alloys are cooled, and this in turn suggests that a fairly low-temperature equilibrium was achieved. Upon reheating the particles dissolve. Because solution is dependent on time and temperature, it is possible to utilize observations of microstructures to estimate the temperature and time involved in reheating.

The authors have used observations such as these in estimating the extent of aerodynamic heating in the Keen Mountain hexahedrite. In this case, the observations were made on schriebersite and rhabdite. These phosphides have a eutectic temperature near 1000 C. Exposure to temperatures in excess of 1000 C causes melting, and rapid cooling results in the formation of a fine two-phase typically eutectic structure. Exposure to temperatures in this range also permits partial solution of the particles. Examples of the appearance of phosphides after heating are given in Figure 8. By comparing the microstructure of specimens heat treated for short times at various temperatures with the structures found in the visible heat-affected zone of the meteorite, it was possible to reconstruct the thermal gradient which once existed in the meteorite. Using the same assumptions employed during the study of the Grant meteorite (Maringer and Manning, 1960) it was possible to make quantitative estimates of both the rate of aerodynamic heating

250X   N56173

a.   10 Seconds at 977 C
(Figure 8)

and the amount of ablation. These data are described in full elsewhere. (Maringer and Manning,
1959b).

Carbides in meteorites (cohenite) will also
tend to break up and go into solution on reheating. An example of this is shown in Figure 9
(for a diamond-bearing specimen of Canyon Diablo
meteorite). From left to right fairly well defined layers of recrystallized kamacite, pearlite,
what appears to be ledeburite (iron-carbon eutec-

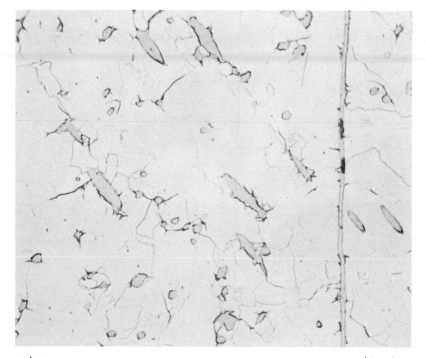

250X   N56174

b. 10 Seconds at 998 C

FIGURE 8.   Effects of artificial heat treatment
             on rhabdite in Keen Mountain Meteor-
             ite.

tic), and cohenite exist. Lipschutz and Anders
(1961) have shown that temperatures in excess
of 1100 C are required to produce the ledeburite
in samples of the Odessa meteorite. From this
they have reasoned that the temperature to which
this particular specimen of Canyon Diablo, which
has a structure remarkably similar to that of
the Odessa, must have been heated was at least
1100 C for a few seconds. Since many of the re-

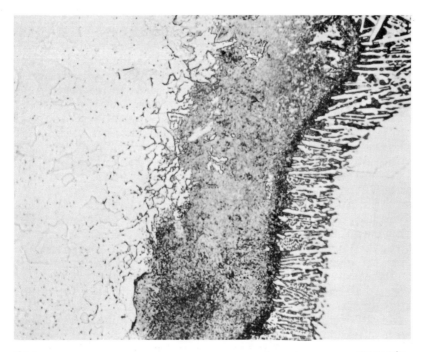

500X   N73759

FIGURE 9.   Diffusion zone between cohenite (on
            the right) and kamacite (on the left)
            in Canyon Diablo Meteorite.

crystallized specimens of Canyon Diablo contain
diamonds, while diamonds have never been found
in any of the uncrystallized fragments, these
authors concluded that the temperatures indicated were those required to form diamonds during
the passage of a shock wave. Although this hypothesis was first suggested by Nininger some
years ago, the work of Lipschutz and Anders is
the first critical analysis of the microstructure in an attempt to support the hypothesis.

The importance of this hypothesis is immediately apparent, for it is no longer possible to consider the existence of diamonds in meteorites as proof that the specimens were formed under high (probably gravitational) static pressures.

There are some additional observations on diamond-bearing Canyon Diablo specimens which are pertinent. These specimens, in addition to having cohenite, also show considerable schrieversite and rhabdite. In scanning a metallographically polished and etched surface, it is immediately obvious that in some areas the phosphides show no evidence of thermal alteration, while in others, only a few centimeters away, fully developed eutectic structures can be observed. Clearly, there must have been a marked thermal gradient within the specimen at one time. The gradient is much too broad to be associated with aerodynamic heating, yet too narrow to be considered the result of nonuniform cooling. Such a gradient, however, might be expected in a specimen due to shock-wave attenuation or interference.

Interestingly enough in one specimen of Canyon Diablo which we have examined, the diamonds appear to have formed on the low-temperature side of the specimen. This would suggest a temperature of formation of 950 C or possibly even lower. This would tend to rule out any hope of diamond formation by a diffusion process in the short time which the specimen was exposed to high pressures. Hence, the diamonds appear to have been formed by the direct transformation of graphite.

Obviously, a more careful study of thermally altered material in Canyon Diablo specimens is necessary in order to get a more accurate picture of the temperatures and temperature distributions involved. Such an investigation is already in progress in our laboratory.

CONCLUSIONS

It is rather amazing that the contribution of the science of metallurgy to the science of meteorites has been so small, when so many possi-

bilities exist. As an example of how little
metallurgy has contributed, it is worthwhile to
point out the system of classification used for
chondritic meteorites. The only way in which
the metal phase enters into this classification
is by being either present or absent. Yet, with
the exception of the gross Widmanstatten pattern,
virtually every type of meteoritic iron, along
with thermal alterations and deformation structures, can be found in chondrites. It would be
possible to construct a system of classification
based on the character of the metallic fragments.
Had some enterprising metallurgist done this
some years ago, we might today have a better understanding of how the many different kinds of
chondrites were formed.

It should be clear by now that the tools, techniques, and ideas which have been so valuable in
advancing our knowledge of terrestrial metallurgy
have very direct applications in meteoritic metallurgy. We have tried to show some of the progress which has been made (there is a great deal
more than has been discussed here), and have at
the same time tried to show where some fertile
ground exists. One might say that some of the
spade work has been done, but the harvest is
still to come.

ACKNOWLEDGMENTS

The authors wish to express their gratitude to
Dr. B. Mason of the American Museum of Natural
History, Mr. E.P. Henderson of the U.S. Museum
of Natural History, and Dr. J.J. Stevens of The
Ohio State University for their generosity in
supplying meteoritic specimens for study and for
many valuable and stimulating discussions on the
subject.

REFERENCES

Lipschutz, M.E. and E.Anders. 1961. Origin of
   Diamonds in Iron Meteorites, Geochim. et Cos-
   mochim. Acta, to be published.
Maringer, R.E. 1960. Ablation Deposits on Iron

Meteorites, Geochim. et Cosmochim. Acta, 19,5.

Maringer, R.E. and G.K. Manning. 1959a. Are Metallic Meteorites a Key to the Re-Entry Problem? Iron Age, 183, 93-96.

Maringer, R.E. and G.K.Manning. 1959b. Aerodynamic Heating of Iron Meteorites During Entry Into the Atmosphere, WADC Technical Report 59-164.

Maringer, R.E. and G.K.Manning. 1960. Aerodynamic Heating of the Grant Meteorite, Geochim et Cosmochim. Acta, 18, 157.

McCall, J.L., private communication.

McQueen, R.G. and S.P. Marsh. 1960. Equation of State for Nineteen Metallic Elements from Short-Wave Measurements to Two Megabars, J. App. Physics, 31, 1253.

Smith, C.S. 1958. Metallographic Studies of Metals after Explosive Shock, Trans. AIME, 212, 574.

BRIAN MASON

The American Museum of Natural History

The Minerals of Meteorites

In 1894 Cohen published the first volume of
his great work, Meteoritenkunde. This volume
gave a comprehensive account, with bibliogra-
phies, of all the minerals described from meteorites up to that time. Nothing as extensive
has been published since, but there are useful
publications by Farrington (1915), Merrill
(1930), Neuerburg (1946,1949), Nininger (1952),
and especially Krinov (1960). The present paper is a summary compilation from all these
sources, combined with additional data from
other publications, personal communications
from Mr. E.P.Henderson, and unpublished researches at this institution.

The minerals known from meteorites at this
time are listed in Table 1. A series of brief
commentaries on these minerals, arranged alpha-
betically, follows.

Alabandite: This mineral was recently identified in meteorites for the first time by
Dawson, Maxwell, and Parsons (1960). They
found it in Abee, an enstatite chondrite. It
was identified in a single chondrule by its
X-ray diffraction pattern, and optically as
round gray metallic inclusions in kamacite-
taenite areas.

The alabanite is associated with oldhamite.

Table 1. The minerals of meteorites (an aster-
isk indicates those not known to occur in terrestrial rocks).

Mineral	Formula
Nickel-iron	(Fe,Ni)
Copper	Cu
Gold	Au
Diamond	C
Graphite	C
Sulphur	S
Moissanite	SiC
Coehnite	Fe_3C
*Schreibersite	$(Fe,Ni)_3P$
*Osbornite	TiN
Troilite	FeS
*Oldhamite	CaS
Alabandite	MnS
Pentlandite	$(Fe,Ni)_9S_8$
*Daubreelite	$FeCr_2S_4$
*Lawrencite	$FeCl_2$
Magnesite	$MgCO_3$
Calcite	$CaCO_3$
Ilmenite	$FeTiO_3$
Magnetite	Fe_3O_4
Chromite	$FeCr_2O_4$
Spinel	$MgAl_2O_4$
Quartz	SiO_2
Tridymite	SiO_2
Cristobalite	SiO_2
Apatite	$Ca_5(PO_4)_3Cl$
*Merrillite	$Na_2Ca_3(PO_4)_2O$
*Farringtonite	$Mg_3(PO_4)_2$
Epsomite	$MgSO_4 \cdot 7H_2O$
Olivine	$(Mg,Fe)_2SiO_4$
Orthopyroxene	$(mg,Fe)SiO_3$
Clinopyroxene	$(Ca,Mg,Fe)SiO_3$
Plagioclase	$(Na,Ca)(Al,Si)_4O_8$
Serpentine	$Mg_6Si_4O_{10}(OH)_8$

These two minerals are isomorphous, and CaS and MnS are probably increasingly miscible with increasing temperatures. The amount of Ca in the alabandite and the amount of Mn in the oldhamite could provide an indication of the temperature of crystallization of these minerals in the meteorite.

Apatite: The phosphate minerals of meteorites are apatite, merrillite, and in one meteorite the recently described farringtonite. The phosphorus content of meteorites is uniformly low, so these minerals are only present in accessory amounts. In appearance and optical properties merrillite and apatite are very similar, and they are almost impossible to distinguish except by tedious and time-consuming techniques. Merrillite has been definitely identified in only three meteorites. If we can assume that the phosphate shown by analyses of stony meteorites is all combined as apatite, then the average P_2O_5 content (0.21%) indicates that they contain about 0.6% apatite. Shannon and Larsen (1925) have analysed the apatite from the New Concord meteorite and have shown that it is a chlorapatite; this is presumably true for other meteorite apatites also.

Calcite: This mineral has been recorded only once in meteorites, in the Boriskino carbonaceous chondrite by Kvasha (1948).

Chromite: The small amount of Cr_2O_3 (average 0.36%) in stony meteorites is normally present as chromite. This mineral has also been recorded in some irons and stony irons (Admire, Coahuila, Marjalahti, Sikhote-Aline). Some of the analyses of meteoritic chromite show considerable amounts of Al_2O_3 (up to 28%) and MgO (up to 21%).

Clinopyroxene: Clinopyroxene of various kinds has been described from meteorites. The pyroxenic achondrites (aubrites and diogenites) show patches of polysynthetically twinned clino-

enstatite or clinohypersthene within the large
fragments of orthorhombic pyroxene; the general
features suggest that the clinopyroxene has resulted from the mechanical deformation of the
orthopyroxene (a mode of formation demonstrated experimentally by Turner, Heard, and Griggs
(1960)).

Monoclinic pyroxenes have been described from
the calcium-rich achondrites, and from some
chondrites and mesosiderites. Such pyroxenes
have usually been referred to as augite; however,
the few analyses that are available show that
the pyroxene is low in CaO, has little Al_2O_3,
and is actually a pigeonite. True augite is
known from only one meteorite, Angra dos Reis.
Diopside which is practically iron-free has been
recorded from the Bustee and Pena Blanca Spring
meteorites; a monoclinic pyroxene intermediate
in composition between diopside and hedenbergite
makes up a large part of the Nakhla meteorite.
Pyroxenes near diopside in composition have been
recorded in small amounts in many chondrites.

Cohenite: This mineral has been recorded as
an accessory constituent in the following iron
meteorites: Bendego, Canyon Diablo, Cosby's
Creek, Cranbourne, Magura, Pittsburg, Wichita
County, and Youngedin. These are all coarse
octahedrites with a nickel content of not more
than 7%; cohenite has apparently not been found
in the higher nickel (medium and fine) octahedrites, nor in the nickel-rich ataxites. It
was recently recorded from the enstatite chondrite Abee (Dawson, Maxwell, and Parsons, 1960),
but has otherwise not been found in the stony-
irons or the stones. However, Perry (1944),
who has given a careful description of the occurrence of cohenite, points out that it is
very difficult to distinguish from schreibersite
and it may therefore be more common than the few
records suggest. Henderson (personal communication) states that it occurs in Coolac, Lexington,
Mooranoppin, Mount Ayliff, Mount Stirling, Odessa, Rosario, St. Francois County, Seligman,
Smithville, Yenberrie (coarse octahedrites),

Gun Creek (medium octahedrite) and Navajo
(nickel-poor ataxite).

Ringwood (1960) has pointed out that the free
energy of cohenite is such that it is unstable
relative to carbon-saturated iron and graphite
at zero pressure at all temperatures below
1153°. It is a stable phase at high pressures.
From the thermodynamic data Ringwood concludes
that all meteorites containing cohenite must
have cooled under pressures exceeding 25,000
atmospheres. However, since the thermodynamic
data are for the iron-carbon system, caution is
indicated in applying these data to meteorites,
in which appreciable amounts of other elements,
especially nickel, are present.

Copper: Small grains of copper have been observed in a few chondrites; Bherai, Carnett,
Miller (Arkansas), Nikolskoe, Ochansk, Rangala,
Richardton, Saratov, Vengerovo. Copper has
been observed in the Morito iron (Nininger,
personal communication). The copper content of
meteorites is low (about 0.01%), so the chances
of observing a grain of copper on a random polished surface is quite small. In reporting the
occurrence of copper in meteorites care must be
taken to avoid the accidental introduction of
copper from copper saw blades or copper polish-
ing laps.

Nininger (1943) has reported the finding, at
Eaton, Colorado, of a meteorite consisting entirely of a copper alloy. The identification
of this specimen as a meteorite has however been
questioned, and further investigation is required before the report is acceptable. However,
Paneth (1951) has drawn attention to a seven-
teenth century report on the fall of copper meteorites.

Cristobalite: This mineral was recently identified in the Abee meteorite, an enstatite chondrite, by Dawson, Maxwell, and Parsons (1960).
It occurred in association with quartz, and was
identified by its X-ray powder pattern, although
it was not detected by optical means. It is the

alpha or low temperature form of this mineral.
Cohen (1900) described an accessory mineral from
the Kendall County iron which he tentatively
identified as cristobalite.

Daubreelite: This mineral was discovered by
J. Lawrence Smith (1876) in the Coahuila meteorite, and has since been observed in many
irons. Perry (1944) remarks that it is commonest in hexahedrites, much less common in other
irons, and that it is usually associated with
troilite, adjoining or bordering it, or inter-
grown with it, frequently in parallel intergrowths. These intergrowths suggest an exsolu-
tion origin. Unlike troilite, daubreelite is
said not to be attacked by hydrochloric acid,
though dissolved by nitric acid.
Daubreelite has been identified in one stony
meteorite, Blithfield, an enstatite chondrite
(Johnston and Connor, 1922). It is probably
present in other enstatite chondrites, which
are in a highly reduced state. In other stony
meteorites, however, the chromium is present in
the oxidized form as chromite.

Diamond: Diamonds were first observed in meteorites by Jerofejeff and Latchinoff (1888),
in the Novo Urei achondrite; this occurrence
has recently been confirmed by Ringwood (1960).
Sandberger (1889) reported that he had observed
a small black diamond in the Carcote chondrite.
Weinschenk (1889) found diamonds in the Magura
iron. Foote (1891) reported diamonds in the
Canyon Diablo iron, and this observation was
confirmed by X-ray diffraction by Ksanda and
Henderson (1939) and subsequently by other investigators. Urey, Mele, and Mayeda (1957)
searched for diamonds in Cape Giradeau, Cold
Bokkeveld, Forest City, Holbrook, Indarch, Richardton, Warrenton (all chondrites), and in
Goalpara (an achondrite similar to Novo Urei);
diamonds were found in Goalpara only. Cubical
aggregates of graphite, known as cliftonite,
have been recorded from Magura, Youngedin, Cosby's Creek, Smithville, and Toluca (all irons);

these are believed to be paramorphs after diamond.

The occurrence of diamonds in meteorites has
been generally interpreted as indicating crystallization under high gravitational pressures in
a meteorite parent body. However, Lipschutz and
Anders (1960) suggest that the diamonds in the
Canyon Diablo meteorite were formed upon impact
with the Earth, and that all meteoritic diamonds
were produced by catastrophic events, either impact with the Earth, or during the breakup of
the meteorite parent bodies.

Epsomite: Berzelius in 1834 observed that the
Alais meteorite, a carbonaceous chondrite, contained some 10% of water-soluble salts, principally magnesium sulphate. Water-soluble salts
have been noted in other carbonaceous chondrites.
Some authorities have claimed that these salts
are not original constituents, but have been
formed after the meteorites reached the Earth
by the action of atmospheric moisture on sulphur
compounds. However, Daubree (1864) showed that
the water-soluble material in Orgueil was an
original constituent of this meteorite. Every
specimen of Orgueil shows a white salt throughout the friable mass of the meteorite; in this
museum the salt is hydrated magnesium sulphate,
$MgSO_4.7H_2O$, according to Du Fresne and Anders
(1961). However, the state of hydration will
vary with the humidity, and the state of hydration when the meteorite was in outer space is
unknown.

Farringtonite: This is a new mineral, anhy-
drous magnesium phosphate, which has recently
been found in the Springwater pallasite by Du-
Fresne and Roy (1960). It occurs in small a-
mounts in this meteorite, peripheral to the
olivine grains.

Gold: Two small (diameter 0.2 mm.) grains of
gold were observed in the Wedderburn iron
(Edwards, 1951). In view of the very low average gold content of iron meteorites (about 1 p.

p.m.) the occurrence of free gold is surprising;
nevertheless, Edwards' description seems to exclude the possibility that the gold was acci-
dently introduced.

Graphite: This is a common accessory mineral
in iron meteorites. It may occur as plates or
grains, but is usually in the form of nodules
which may reach considerable size - one nodule
in Cosby's Creek was as large as a small pear
and weighed 92 grams. The graphite is frequently intimately associated with troilite. Graphite has been recognized by X-ray powder photographs in the achondrites Goalpara (Urey, Mele,
and Mayeda, 1957) and Novo Urei (Ringwood, 1960).
The peculiar group of carbonaceous chondrites
contain free carbon in amounts up to 5%. This
carbon has been identified as graphite. However, it is amorphous to X-rays and appears to
be a non-crystalline "soot", or possibly a py-
robitumen. Much of the free carbon in iron and
stony-iron meteorites lacks the characteristic
properties of graphite and may also be amorphous.

Ilmenite: This mineral has been recorded in a
few stony meteorites, for example Breitscheid,
Sevrukovo, Padvarninkai, Vengerovo, Yurtuk. It
may be more common than has been realized. However, the titanium content in stony meteorites
is generally low (average TiO_2 in 94 chondrites
is 0.11%), and much of this may be present in
silicate minerals, so the amount of ilmenite
will always be small.

Lawrencite: The exudation of drops of ferrous
chloride solution from freshly cut or broken
surfaces of iron meteorites was early noted, but
it was not until 1855 that J. Lawrence Smith
found the mineral as a soft solid of green-brown
color in the Tazewell iron. The solid mineral
has also been reported in the Laurens County and
Smith's Mountain irons. Henderson (personal
communication) has observed it in several pallasites and in the Odessa and Sardis irons.
Little description of the appearance of the min-

eral has been given; it is simply stated that
it occurred in crevices and became soft on exposure. Ferrous chloride is deliquescent and
decomposes in air to give ferric hydroxide
(limonite) and hydrochloric acid, which immediately attacks the meteoritic iron, causing
"sweating" and rapid disintegration. Some irons,
such as Cranbourne, are particularly subject to
this disintegrations; the specimen of Cranbourne
in the British Museum is kept in a closed glass
case in an atmosphere of dry nitrogen. Small
amounts of lawrencite are probably present in
many stone meteorites, since on cutting or
breaking they frequently become rust-brown or
freckled with rust-colored spots.

Magnesite: Pisani (1864) identified the fer-
roan variety of magnesite, known as breunnerite,
as a minor constituent of the Orgueil meteorite,
a carbonaceous chondrite. It occurred in small
amounts in minute rhombohedral crystals. I recently extracted a few grains of this mineral
from the Orgueil meteorite by the use of heavy
liquids; it gave the X-ray powder pattern of
magnesite, and the omega refractive index was
1.74, indicating a content of about 20 mol per
cent of the $FeCO_3$ component.
This mineral has been identified in Boriskino,
another carbonaceous chondrite, by Kvasha (1948).

Magnetite: This mineral is an important constituent in many of the carbonaceous chondrites.
X-ray powder photographs of the Type I carbonaceous chondrites of Wiik (1956) - Alais, Ivuna,
Orgueil and Tonk -show lines of magnetite only.
Magnetite has been recorded in the achondrites
Shergotty and Padvarninkai. In chondrites it is
recorded as a constituent of the glassy crust
formed furing the passage of the meteorite
through the atmosphere. Magnetite probably
forms as a secondary mineral in some meteorites
by the oxidation of nickel-iron after the meteorite has fallen.

Merrillite: In 1883 Tschermak described the
occurrence in the groundmass of chondritic meteorites of a colorless accessory mineral, as
optically biaxial grains with weak double re-
fraction; he was unable to identify it but suggested that it might be monticellite. Wherry
(1917) applied the name merrillite to it, but
it was first separated and chemically analysed
by Shannon and Larsen (1925). They gave it the
formula $NaCa_3(PO_4)_2O$, but the analysis was made
on a very small amount of material; no X-ray
investigations of the mineral have been reported.
Merrillite may be identical with or closely related to the terrestrial mineral dehrnite, a
calcium sodium phosphate isostructural with
apatite.

Moissanite: This mineral, naturally occurring
carborundum, was found by Moissan (1904) in the
residue left after dissolving a 53 kilogram
piece of the Canyon Diablo iron in hydrochloric
acid, and treating this residue with hydroflu-
oric acid and boiling sulphuric acid. The mineral occurred as small hexagonal crystals varying in color from pale green to emerald green;
it was unattacked by acid but gave potassium
silicate on fusion with KOH and CO_2 on fusion
with $PbCrO_4$. In physical and chemical properties the mineral agreed with the previously
known and artificially produced carborundum.
Merrill (1930) comments "the fact that meteoric
irons are commonly sawn by crushed carborundum
raises a doubt as to the actual meteoric source
of this material." I recently dissolved 1 kilogram of Canyon Diablo in hydrochloric acid and
found no moissanite in the residue. The occurrence of this material as a meteoritic mineral
is doubtful and needs confirmation.

Nickel-iron: This is almost omnipre-
sent constituent of meteorites. The siderites
consist almost entirely of nickel-iron; it is a
major constituent of the stony-irons; the chondrites average about 13% of metal, the content
ranging from 1% to 25%. Only the carbonaceous

chondrites and some of the achondrites have no
free metal or only trace amounts.

The nickel-iron occurs as two distinct minerals, kamacite and taenite. Kamacite, the alpha-
iron of the metallurgist, is a nickel-iron alloy
with a fairly constant composition of 5.5% Ni;
it crystallizes in a body-centred cubic lattice.
Taenite, the gamma-iron of the metallurgist, is
a nickel-iron alloy of variable composition,
ranging from about 13% to about 65% Ni in different meteorites; it crystallizes in a face-
centred cubic lattice. Butectoid intergrowths
of kamacite and taenite, known as plessite, are
present in many meteorites. A thorough account
of meteoritic nickel-iron is given by Perry
(1944).

Oldhamite: This mineral was described by
Maskelyne (1870) in the Bustee meteorite. It
occurred as chestnut-brown rounded spherules up
to 6 mm. in diameter. It is readily attached
by water with the formation of gypsum, and its
presence in a meteorite can be established by
boiling a powdered sample in water and testing
the solution for calcium and sulphate.

Oldhamite has been recorded in the following
meteorites: Abee, Aubres, Bishopville, Bustee,
Indarch, and Hvittis. It is probably present
in accessory amounts in most, if not all, enstatite chondrites and enstatite achondrites.

Olivine: This mineral is an essential component of several groups of meteorites: the pallasites are composed of nickel-iron and olivine;
it is a major constituent in all the chondrites,
except the enstatite chondrites and some of the
carbonaceous chondrites; and it is present in
many achondrites. In composition it is usually
a magnesium-rich variety with between 10 and 30
mol percent of the Fe_2SiO_4 component; pure forsterite (Mg_2SiO_4) has been recorded from the
Shallowater and Pena Blanca Spring meteorites,
both aubrites (enstatite achondrites), and in
Pine River and Tucson (irons); a forsterite with
6 mol percent Fe_2SiO_4 component, according to

the analysis of Prior (1912).

Orthopyroxene: This mineral, next to olivine, is the commonest silicate mineral in meteorites. It is a major constituent of most chondrites, and is an important mineral in the mesosiderites and the calcium-poor achondrites. The orthopyroxene is usually distinguished as enstatite, bronzite, or hypersthene according to its iron content; with less than 10 mol percent of the $FeSiO_3$ component it is enstatite, with 10-20% bronzite, and with more than 20% hypersthene. The sequence is not continuous in meteorite orthopyroxene, however; as Farrington (1915) noted, the enstatite is generally close to $MgSiO_3$ in composition, and pyroxenes between this and bronzite are lacking. Nor does the composition range extend to iron-dominated orthopyroxene; the hypersthene from meteorites seldom exceeds 30 mol percent $FeSiO_3$.

Osbornite: This mineral was described by Maskelyne (1870) as minute yellow octahedrons in the Bustee meteorite. On account of the very small amount, Maskelyne was unable to determine its composition. Bannister (1941) showed that it is titanium nitride, TiN. It has not been recognized in any other meteorite.

Pentlandite: This mineral was recently identified in the Kaba meteorite, a carbonaceous chondrite, by Sztrokay (1960). I have found it in Karoonda, a meteorite rather similar to Kaba in chemical and mineralogical composition. Jeremine, Lelubre, and Sandrea (1956) identified minute plates of pentlandite enclosed in troilite in the Isoulane chondrite.

Plagioclase: This mineral is a common constituent, in small amounts, of many of the stony meteorites. Michel (1912) has written an extensive account of meteoritic plagioclase. In most chondrites it is present in about 5 - 10%; the composition is usually oligoclase, but anorthite contents ranging from 5% - 34% have

been recorded. In feldspar-bearing achondrites
the plagioclase is usually bytownite or anorthite, the albite content being about 10%.

Tschermak (1872) identified and described a
colorless isotropic material in the Shergotty
meteorite, which he named maskelynite. Maskelynite is a glass of plagioclase composition,
hence, is not a true mineral in terms of the
definition of a mineral as a crystalline substance. It has been found in a number of chondrites; sometimes it is associated with plagioclase grains. Whether it has been formed by the
fusion of pre-existing plagioclase or whether
the plagioclase is crystallized maskelynite is
not clear.

Quartz: This mineral has been identified in
the insoluble residues of a number of iron meteorites, originally by Rose in 1861. Doubts
have been expressed as to the extra-terrestrial
origin of this quartz, some workers believing
that the quartz is detrital grains embedded in
the surface crust of these meteorites. Quartz
was doubtfully identified in the St. Marks stone
by Cohen (1906) and confirmed by Merrill (1924).
This quartz is within the body of the meteorite
and is certainly part of its extra-terrestrial
composition. Quartz has been identified, always
in accessory amounts, in the eucrites Chaves,
Jonzac, Peramiho, and Stannern (Berwerth, 1912),
and in the enstatite chondrite Abee (Dawson,
Maxwell, and Parsons, 1960).

Schreibersite: This mineral was described and
named by Haidinger in 1847 as a constituent of
the Magura iron, and seems to be universally
present as an accessory mineral in iron meteorites. It also occurs in the stony-irons, but
its presence in the stones has not been confirmed - in these the phosphorus is present as phosphate, except perhaps in the enstatite chondrites.

Schreibersite commonly occurs in thin plates,
often oriented in the same directions as the
kamacite and taenite lamellae in the Widmanstat-

ten structure; this variety is called rhabdite
and was formerly believed to be a distinct mineral. It also occurs as a shell around nodules
of troilite. The color is tin-white when fresh,
but it tarnishes readily to bronze-yellow. The
mineral is brittle, magnetic, and almost insoluble in acids. Numerous analyses of schreibersite and rhabdite have been made, all indicating
a formula $(Fe,Ni)_3P$; the Fe:Ni ratio ranges from
about 7:1 to 5:3.

Serpentine: As long ago as 1860, Wohler suggested that the silicate material of Cold Bokkeveld, a carbonaceous chondrite, consisted
largely of serpentine. This observation was
overlooked or disbelieved for many years. Kvasha (1948) identified chlorite or serpentine in
the Boriskino carbonaceous chondrite, and later
in the Mighei carbonaceous chondrite also. It
seems to be characteristic of the Type II carbonaceous chondrites of Wiik (1956) and I have
identified it in the following meteorites of
this type: Cold Bokkeveld, Erakot, Haripura,
Murray, Nawapali, Nogoya, and Santa Cruz.
The identification of this mineral as serpentine rather than chlorite rests on the following
grounds: (a) X-ray powder photographs do not
show the 14A reflection characteristic of chlorite; (b) the bulk composition of the meteorites
in which it occurs is very low in Al_2O_3 (about
2%) - if the mineral were chlorite the Al_2O_3
content should be much higher. Unfortunately,
the mineral is very fine-grained and intimately
mixed with amorphous carbon, which makes it impossible to determine its optical properties.

Spinel: This mineral was recently identified
in the Kaba meteorite, a carbonaceous chondrite,
by Sztrokay (1960). I have recently found it in
Vigarano, a carbonaceous chondrite very similar
to Kaba. In both these meteorites it is present
in very small amounts, and has been identified
by its optical properties and its X-ray powder
photograph.
Foote (1912) recorded red-brown spinel in the

Holbrook chondrite; Merrill (1912) was unable to
confirm this, nor were Mason and Wiik (1961);
the latter suggest that this material was chromite.

Sulphur: Sulphur in the amount of 1% or more
can be extracted by carbon disulphide, or other
solvents, from some carbonaceous chondrites,
Alais, Cold Bokkeveld, and Orgueil for example.
Although the sulphur has not been recognized as
discrete particles in these extremely fine-
grained meteorites, there is little reason to
doubt that it exists therein in the free state.

Tridymite: This mineral is not uncommon as an
accessory in the calcium-rich achondrites; it
has been observed in Moore County, Pasamonte,
Chaves, and Juvinas. It has also been recorded
from the stony-irons Steinback, Vaca Muerta, and
Crab Orchard, and from the enstatite chondrite
Indarch. Since tridymite is not stable above
about 3000 kg/cm^2 pressure at any temperature,
its presence in these meteorites places a severe
restriction on their conditions of crystallization.

Troilite: This mineral is present in accessory amounts in practically all meteorites. It
is difficult to estimate the average amount in
iron meteorites, since the troilite usually occurs as comparatively large nodules very irregu-
larly distributed; in the chondritic meteorites
the mineral occurs as small grains randomly distributed, and the amount seems fairly constant,
averaging about 6% by weight. The presence of
free iron in meteorites would appear to ensure
that the composition of troilite is stochio-
metric FeS, with no deficiency of iron as in
terrestrial pyrrhotite. Curvello (1958) has
given a detailed account of the mode of occurrence of troilite in several irons.

References

Bannister, F.A. 1941. Osbornite, meteoritic titanium nitride. Min. Mag., 26, 36-44.

Berwerth, F. 1912. Quarz und Tridymit als Ge-
mengteile der meteorischen Eukrite. Sitzber.
Akad. Wiss. Wien, 121, 763-783.

Berzelius, J. J. 1834. Om meteorstenar. Handl.
Svenska Vetenskaps-Akad., 115-183.

Cohen, E. 1894. Meteoritenkunde. Heft 1: Unter-
suchungsmethoden und Charakteristik der Ge-
mengtheil. E. Schweizerbart'sche Verlagshand-
lung, Stuttgart.

Cohen, E. 1900. Meteoreisen-Studien XI. Ann.
k.k. Hofmus. Wien, 15, 351-391.

Cohen, E. 1906. On the meteoric stone which fell
at the mission station of St. Mark's Transkei,
on January 3, 1903. Annals South African Mus.,
5, 1-16.

Curvello, W. S. 1958. Meteoritic sulphides.
Bol. Mus. Nacional (Brazil), Geologia, (27).

Daubree, A. 1864. Note sur les meteorites tom-
bees le 14 Mai aux environs d'Orgueil (Tarn-
et-Garonne). Compt. Rend. Acad. Sci. Paris,
58, 985-990.

Dawson, K., J. A. Maxwell, and D. E. Parsons.
1960. A description of the meteorite which
fell near Abee, Alberta, Canada. Geochim.
Cosmochim. Acta, 21, 127-144.

Da Fresne, E. R., and S. K. Roy. 1960. A new
phosphate mineral from the Springwater pallasite. Enrico Fermi Institute for Nuclear
Studies, University of Chicago, Publication
60-54.

Du Fresne, E. R., and E. Anders. 1961. The record in the meteorites. V. A thermometer mineral in the Mighei carbonaceous chondrite. Geochim. Cosmochim. Acta, 23, 200-208.

Edwards, A. B. 1953. The Wedderburn meteoritic
iron. Proc. Roy. Soc. Victoria, 64, 73-76.

Farrington, O. C. 1915. Meteorites. Published by
the author, Chicago.

Foote, A. E. 1891. A new locality for meteoric
iron with a preliminary notice of the discovery of diamonds in the iron. Proc. Am.

Assoc. Adv. Sci., 40, 279-283.

Foote, W. M. 1912. Preliminary note on the
    shower of meteoric stones near Holbrook, Nava-
    jo County, Arizona. Am. J. Sci., 34, 437-456.

Haidinger, W. 1847. Uber das Meteoreisen von
    Braunau. Ann. Physik., 72, 580-82.

Jeremine, E., M. Lelubre, and A. Sandrea. 1956.
    La meteorite d'Isoulane-n-Amahar (nord-nord-
    est de Fort Polignac, confins Algero-Fezza-
    nais). Compte. Rend. Acad. Sci. Paris, 242,
    2369-2372.

Jerofejeff, N., and P. A. Latchinoff. 1888.
    Meteorite diamantifere tombee le 10/22 sep-
    tembre 1886, en Russie, a Novo-Urei, gouverne-
    ment de Penza. Compt. Rend. Acad. Sci. Paris,
    106, 1679-1681.

Johnson, R. A. A., and M. R. Conner, 1922. The
    Blithfield meteorite. Trans. Roy. Soc. Canada,
    16, 187-193.

Kvasha, L. G. 1948. An investigation of the
    stony meteorite Staroe Boriskino. Meteoritika,
    4, 83-96.

Krinov, E. L. 1960. Principles of Meteoritics.
    Pergamon Press, New York.

Ksanda, C. J., and E. P. Henderson. 1939. Iden-
    tification of diamond in the Canyon Diablo
    iron. Am. Min., 24, 677-680.

Lipschutz, M. E., and E. Anders. 1960. The re-
    cord in the meteorites IV. Origin of diamonds
    in iron meteorites. Enrico Fermi Institute
    for Nuclear Studies, University of Chicago,
    Publ. 60-32.

Maskelyne, N. S. 1870. On the mineral constitu-
    ents of meteorites. Phil. Trans. Roy. Soc.,
    160, 189-214.

Mason, B., and Wiil, H. B. 1961. The Holbrook,
    Arizona, chondrite. Geochim. Cosmochim. Acta,
    21, 276-283.

Merrill, G. P. 1912. A recent meteorite fall
    near Holbrook, Navajo County, Arizona. Smith-
    sonian Misc. Coll., 60, (9).

Merrill, G. P. 1915. On the monticellite-like
    mineral in meteorites, and on oldhamite as a
    meteoric constituent. Proc. Nat. Acad. Sci.,
    1, 302-308.

Merrill, G. P. 1924. Quartz in meteoric stones. Am. Min., 9, 112-113.

Merrill, G. P. 1930. Composition and structure of meteorites. U.S. Nat. Mus. Bull., 149.

Michel, H. 1912. Die Feldspate der Meteoriten. Min. Pet. Mitt., 31, 563-658.

Moissan, H. 1904. Nouvelles recherches sur la meteorite de Canon Diablo. Compt. Rend. Acad. Sci. Paris, 139, 773-780.

Neuerburg, G. J. 1946. A preliminary note on the exclusively meteoritic minerals. Pop. Astron., 54, 248-255.

Neuerburg, G. J. 1949. A second note on the exclusively meteoritic minerals. Pop. Astron., 57, 342-343.

Nininger, H. H. 1943. The Eaton, Colorado meteorite: introducing a new type. Pop. Astron., 51, 273-280.

Nininger, H. H. 1952. Out of the sky. University of Denver Press.

Paneth, F. A. 1951. A 17th century report on copper meteorites. Geochim. Cosmochim. Acta, 1, 117-118.

Perry, S. H. 1944. The metallography of meteoric iron. U.S. Nat. Mus. Bull., 184.

Pisani, F. 1864. Etude chemique et analyse de l'aerolithe d'Orgueil. Comp. Rend. Acad. Sci. Paris, 59, 132-135.

Prior, G. T. 1912. The meteoric stones of El Nakhla El Baharia (Egypt). Min. Mag., 16, 274-281.

Ringwood, A.E. 1960. The Novo Urei meteorite. Geochim. Cosmochim. Acta, 20, 1-4.

Ringwood, A. E. 1960. Cohenite as a pressure indicator in iron meteorites. Geochim. Cosmochim. Acta, 20, 155-158.

Sandberger, F. 1889. Ein neuer meteorit aus Chile. Neues Jahrb. Min. Geol. Palaont., 2, 173-180.

Shannon, E. F., and E. S. Larson. 1925. Merrillite and chlorapatite from stony meteorites. Am. J. Sci., 9, 250-260.

Smith, J. L. 1855. A description of five new meteoric irons, with some theoretical considerations on the origin of meteorites based on their physical and chemical characters. Am. J. Sci., 19, 322-343.

Smith, J. L. 1876. Aragonite on the surface of a meteoric iron, and a new mineral (daubree-lite) in the concretions of the interior of the same. Am. J. Sci., 12, 107-110.

Sztrokay, K. I. 1960. Über einige Meteoriten-mineralien des kohlenwasserstoffhaltigen Chon-rites von Kaba, Ungarn. Neues Jahrb. Min. Abh., 94, 1284-1294.

Tschermak, G. 1872. Die meteoriten von Shergot-ty und Gopalpur. Sitzber. Akad. Wiss. Wien, 65, 122-146.

Tschermak, G. 1883. Beitrag zur classification der meteoriten. Sitzber. Akad. Wiss. Wien, 88, 347-371.

Turner, F. J., H. Heard, and O. T. Griggs. 1960. Experimental deformation of enstatite and ac-companying inversion to clinoenstatite. Proc. Intern. Geol. Congress, XXI Session, 18, 399-408.

Urey, H. C., A. Mele, and T. Mayeda. 1957. Dia-monds in stone meteorites. Geochim. Cosmochim. Acta, 13, 1-4.

Weinschenk, E. 1889. Uber einig Bestandtheile des meteoreisens von Magura, Arva, Ungarn. Ann. k. k. naturhist. Hofmus. Wien, 4, 94-101.

Wherry, E. T. 1917. Merrillite, meteoritic cal-cium phosphate. Am. Min., 2, 119.

Wiik, H. B. 1956. The chemical composition of some stony meteorites. Geochim. Cosmochim. Acta, 9, 279-289.

Wohler, F. 1860. Neuere untersuchungen uber die Bestandtheile des Meteorsteines vom Capland. Sitzber. Akad. Wiss. Wien, 41, 565-567.

CARLETON B. MOORE

Arizona State University

The Petrochemistry

of the Achondrites

Achondrites account for only about 4.2% of the recognized meteorites. Compared with the chondrites which comprise about 51% of the known meteorites, this number is relatively small.

The achondrite nomenclature like that for igneous rocks leaves much to be desired. Most compilations are classified according to Prior's (1916) revision of the Rose-Chermak-Brezina System. Although the rock names are not important in this paper, the classification in Table 1 patterned after F. C. Leonard (1956) is used. Also included in the table are the number of representatives in each class up to 1956 and the number of representatives in each class from the achondrites with good chemical analyses discussed in this paper.

Although achondrites have greater differences among themselves in their chemical and mineralogical make-up than do the chondrites, as individuals they are much simpler systems than the chondrites and are similar to terrestrial rocks in their appearance. Along with the iron and some of the stony-iron meteorites, they appear to be more likely candidates to be simple equilibrium systems than do the complex chondrites.

To be acceptable, any theory on the origin of achondrites must explain all their properties including their chemical composition, minerology,

164

Table 1.   Classification of Achondrites after
            Leonard (1956)

	Total number known	Number in this paper
1. Amphoterite-olivine hypersthene achondrite	9	2
2. Angrite-augite achondrite	1	1
3. Bustite (Aubrite)-clinoenstatite-enstatite achondrite	5	4
4. Chassignite-olivine achondrite	1	0
5. Chladnite (Diogenite)-hypersthene ach.	5	5
6. Eucrite (anorthite-pigeonite achondrite (anorthite-hedenbergite clino-hypersthene achondrite	18	13
7. Sherghottite (andesine-diopside-clino-hypersthene ach. (andesine-pigeonite ach.	1	1
8. Howardite - anorthite-clinohypersthene-hypersthene ach.	17	9
9. Nakhlite - olivine-hedenbergite-diopside ach.	1	1
10. Nortonite - olivine-enstatite ach.	1	1
11. Ureilite- olivine clinobronzite ach.	3	1
Unclassified achondrites	6	2

petrography, and age relationships. Some of
these properties have been investigated more completely than others. This paper is concerned
primarily with the major element compositions
and the clues they give towards establishing any
petrologic evolution of the achondrites. It does
not take into consideration other properties as
completely as might be desired mainly because of
the scarcity of such data for a suitable number
of individuals.

Of the 66 reported achondrites, Urey and Craig
(1953) were only able to classify the chemical
analyses of 38 of them as superior. Even these
superior analyses are far from good and the only
four components that may be used in petrochemical
comparisons with a degree of confidence appear
to be SiO_2, FeO, MgO and CaO. The data for
Al_2O_3 is fair, but for the alkalis and other
constituents the data is useful only for giving
us some idea of their general amounts.

Most previous studies of the achondrites as a
group, rather than as individuals, have either
averaged their chemical compositions in order to
use them as a small part of a larger picture or
have been involved in developing a meteorite
classification scheme. A notable contribution
not in the above category includes that of Buddington (1943) who compared achondrites and terrestrial rocks, especially with regard to their
MgO/FeO ratios and mineral compositions, in order
to develop his ideas on concepts of the interior
of the earth. C. E. Tilley (1950) also makes
reference to the similarities between achondrites
and terrestrial rocks in his paper on some aspects of magmatic evolution. Both of these authors
do not include all of the types of achondrites in
making their analogies but select only those where
a direct comparison is apparent.

Cassidy (1958) in a paper on "Achondrite investigations and their bearing on the origin of tektites"
reached the conclusion that the variations he observed in achondrites could not have been produced by crystal fractionation in a basic magma,
but might have been produced by a partition of
chemical components due to liquid immiscibility

in such basic magma. He also considered the possibility that the variations could have been produced by crystal fractionation in an extremely
acidic magma but the acidic magma itself would
have to have been produced by a segregation due
to liquid immiscibility.

The chemical analyses of the silicate portions
of the achondrites used in this paper are given
in Table II. Most of them are from the compila-

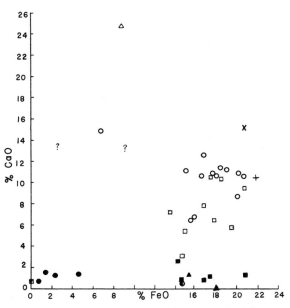

Figure 1. Diagram showing the variation of weight
percent CaO with FeO in the silicate phase of
selected achondrites.

tion of Urey and Craig (1953) including Calivo
and Pampa del Infierno which they discarded.
The analysis of Norton County is taken from Wiik
(1956). Only the values for SiO_2, MgO, FeO,
Al_2O_3, CaO, Na_2O, K_2O in the total silicate have
been included.

If an attempt is made to find any possible
chemical relationships among the achondrites,
by constructing variation diagrams, some interesting results appear.

TABLE II   ANALYSES OF SILICATE FRACTION OF ACHONDRITES
(Total silicate = 100%)

NAME	TYPE	SiO_2	MgO	FeO	Al_2O_3	CaO	Na_2O	K_2O
Angra dos Reis	Ang.	44.49	10.17	8.66	8.84	24.81	0.26	0.19
Atsuma-Mura	-	48.40	8.59	2.57	24.62	13.55	1.54	0.21
Bereba	Euc.	48.80	6.54	18.88	12.33	11.19	0.15	0.22
Binda	Euc.	51.20	16.37	15.50	8.96	6.23	0.28	0.13
Bishopville	Bus.	58.87	34.59	1.31	1.77	1.54	1.06	0.09
Bustee	Bus.	54.81	38.69	4.44		1.22		
Cachau	Euc.	48.53	6.85	20.0	13.95	8.63	0.92	0.13
Calivo	-	49.30	1.54	9.10	19.92	13.20	0.93	0.32
Chewany Kut	Euc.	48.62	6.88	18.22	13.26	11.32	0.51	0.12
Ellemeet	Amp.	53.38	25.53	17.92				
Frankfort	How.	52.22	17.89	13.42	8.19	7.15	0.46	0.22
Goalpara	Ure.	43.99	40.82	14.52		0.654		
Ibbenbuhren	Chl.	54.08	26.07	17.21	1.15	1.20		
Johnstown	Chl.	51.42	27.47	14.07	2.40	2.69	0.34	0.10
Jonzac	Euc.	48.74	7.49	17.91	12.84	10.57	0.92	0.22
Juvinas	Euc.	49.35	6.85	17.57	13.48	10.79	0.40	0.17
LeTeilleul	How.	48.34	13.98	16.78	11.39	7.91	0.22	0.24
Luotolox	How.	47.72	8.61	18.43	13.32	10.33	0.29	
Macikine	Euc.	50.11	8.60	16.31	11.95	10.52	0.63	0.06
Manegaon	Chl.	54.56	22.87	20.61		1.46		
Massing	How.	53.82	8.59	19.24	8.31	5.86	1.96	1.21
Moore County	Euc.	48.23	8.42	15.04	15.59	11.09	0.45	0.09
Nakhla	Nak.	49.01	12.02	20.68	1.74	15.18	0.41	0.14
Norton County	Nor.	55.58	41.64	0.00	0.62	0.67	0.13	0.04
Padvarninkai	Euc.	48.61	9.27	16.65	10.80	12.54	1.24	0.89
Pampadel Inferno	How.	44.00	22.70	14.79	13.53	3.06	0.65	0.08
Pasamonte	How.	49.68	6.67	17.56	14.33	10.55	0.32	0.06
Pavlovka	How.	51.75	14.93	17.71	6.41	6.34	2.07	0.44
Pena Blanca Spring	Bus.	58.28	38.34	2.01	0.21	1.09		
Peramiho	Euc.	49.51	7.17	20.06	11.28	10.88	0.40	0.25
Petersburg	How.	49.89	8.24	20.69	11.20	9.13	0.83	
Roda	Amp.	51.27	27.57	15.17	2.91	1.44	0.30	0.32
Serra de Mage	Euc.	44.38	3.26	6.72	27.87	14.88	1.63	0.20
Shalka	Chl.	52.15	28.15	16.69	0.66	0.88	0.22	
Shallowater	Bus.	58.22	39.32	0.79	0.28	0.53	0.24	0.05
Shergbotly	She.	50.09	9.08	21.80	5.89	10.38	1.28	0.57
Stannern	Euc.	48.56	7.23	20.31	11.33	10.49	0.76	0.13
Tataouine	Chl.	55.55	27.72	14.51	0.63	0.76		
Yurtuk	Euk.	49.64	17.47	15.67	9.70	6.42	0.31	
Zmenj	How.	49.18	17.16	14.96	8.23	5.59	1.79	0.39

In Figures 1 through 4, two component, weight
percent, variation diagrams are shown for the
systems FeO-CaO, MgO-CaO, MgO-FeO and CaO-SiO$_2$.
Diagrams for the other possible combinations including Al$_2$O$_3$ were constructed but they did not
appear to reveal any additional significant information. On the diagrams the achondrites classified by Urey and Craig (1953) as "basaltic"
are shown with open symbols and those classified
as chondritic achondrites are shown with closed
symbols. The basaltic and chondritic type achondrites were characterized by their high and low
calcium contents.

The distributions in Figures 1, 2, and 3 indicate that each of the two major groups appears
to be made up of two subgroups. These are characterized by the following properties.

The chondritic type achondrite-iron-poor group
has less than 5% FeO.

The chondritic type achondrite-iron-rich group
has from 14 to 21% FeO. This group appears to
have more nearly the composition of the average
chondrite.

The basaltic type achondrite-lower-magnesium-
higher calcium-higher aluminum group is different from the basaltic type achondrite-higher
magnesium-lower calcium-lower aluminum group in
the properties used to describe each group.

The latter three groups appear to be more
closely related to each other than do the first
two groups. In other words, some of the chondritic type achondrites and all of the basaltic
type achondrites are greatly different from the
remaining chondritic type achondrites. This
generalization does not include the five achondrites that do not seem to fit into any of the
four groups.

The three groups that are closely related
could conceivably be formed by fractionation in
a silicate melt. The appearance of a new mineral phase could cause the apparent discontinuities.
The achondrites in the chondritic type-high iron
group are mostly chladnites composed of hypersthene (Mg,Fe)SiO$_3$ and amphoterites made up of
olivine (Mg,Fe)$_2$SiO$_4$ and hypersthene. Neither

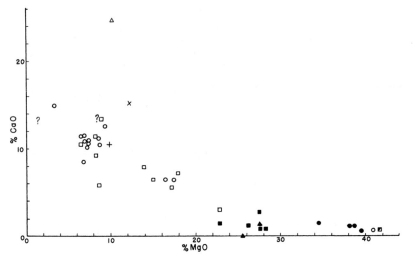

Figure 2.   Diagram showing the variation of
weight percent CaO with MgO in the silicate
phase of selected achondrites.

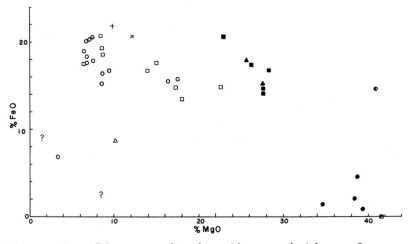

Figure 3.   Diagram showing the variation of
weight percent FeO with MgO in the silicate
phase of selected achondrites.

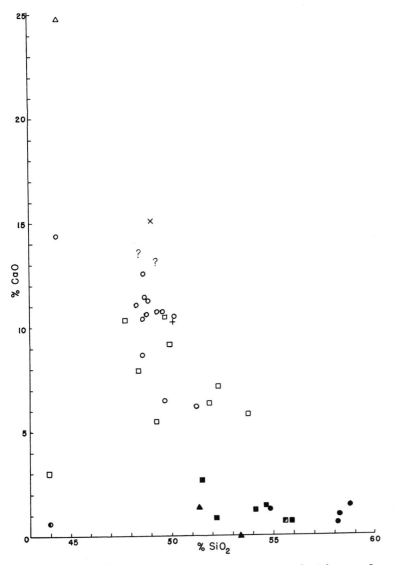

Figure 4.   Diagram showing the variation of
weight percent CaO with SiO$_2$ in the silicate
phase of selected achondrites.

olivine nor hypersthene contain appreciable a-
mounts of calcium. Of the six achondrites making up the basaltic type-higher magnesium-lower
calcium group, four are classified as howardites
containing hypersthene, clinohypersthene and
anorthite ($CaAl_2Si_2O8$) and the other two are
classified as eucrites characterized by clino-
hypersthene-hedenbergite ($(Ca,Fe)SiO_3$ or augite
$Ca(Mg,Fe,Al)(Al,Si)_2O_6$ and anorthite. We notice
the main difference between these first two
groups is the appearance of the calcium-rich
phase anorthite. The basaltic type-lower mag-
nesium-higher calcium achondrite group is made
up of ten eucrites, four howardites, one sher-
ghottite and one nakhlite. This group is generally different from the other basaltic type
group because of the higher proportion of calcium rich pyroxenes. The phase distinction is
not clear-cut however and it is further confused
by the presence of howardites in both groups.
In all probability this results from a difference in the definition for howardites and eucrites among different investigators. The individual achondrites were studied and named
over an approximately one hundred year span and
it would not be surprising if there are incon-
sistencies in the nomenclature. It may also be
true that the mineralogical criteria used in
distinguishing the two types are not valid in a
chemical sense. Yavnell (1956) reached a similar conclusion in his paper on meteorite classification.

A sequence of the appearance of the mineral
phases as outlined above is consistent with both
the phase relationships found in analogous artificial systems and ultrabasic and basic provinces
in the earth's crust. Figure 4 the $CaO-SiO_2$
diagram does not show any evidence to contradict
such a mechanism. The apparent anomaly in the
diagram is due to the fact that only pyroxenes
are crystallized and the molecular SiO_2 ratio
is not varying to any large extent, so that as
MgO is removed from the melt the concentration
by weight percent of SiO_2 appears to decrease.
Such a decrease would not appear on a Mol. %

diagram.

The relationship of the chondritic type low iron achondrites to the other three groups is not as straightforward. The differentiating property is the low iron content and no probable igneous mechanism observed in terrestrial rocks or in artificial systems can be used to produce an essentially pure enstatite, $MgSiO_3$ achondrite from a melt of chondritic composition. The melt from which an enstatite chondrite, bustite, crystallizes must be of a composition fairly close to the final rock.

The simplest answer would then be that these two groups of chondritic type achondrites were separated in another type of reaction before igneous differentiation took place. The two starting melts would then be one essentially of enstatite composition in which a little melt fractionation took place and one with a more ferrous initial composition in which fractionation took place to form the basaltic type achondrites.

Figure 5 is a three component variation diagram for the system CaO-FeO-MgO. These three components show the most variability in the achondrites. The conclusions reached on the basis of the two component diagrams are strengthened by the points distribution on the three component diagram. The main fractionation trend is shown in the lower central part of the diagram. The howardite at (MgO-56, FeO-36,CaO-8) is Pampa del Infierno. This achondrite was discarded in their compilitation by Urey and Craig because it did not "agree" with other representatives of its group. From Figure 5 we may see that it is in the main fractionation sequence and is transitional between two groups.

The positions of those achondrites that did not fit into groups of the two component diagrams now begin to show some relationship to the overall picture. It is possible that they are related to the MgO rich bustites and were formed from the residual material after most of the enstatite melt had crystallized. The direction of composition change for residual melt in both systems is shown in the diagram.

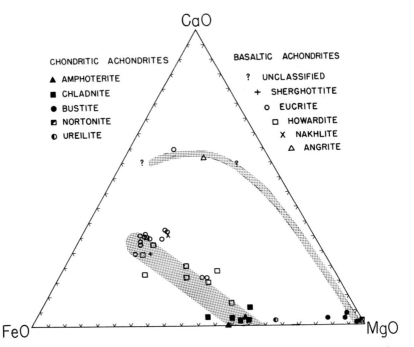

Figure 5. Variation diagram for weight percent CaO, MgO and FeO in the silicate phase of selected achondrites showing the possible fractionation trends for the two general groups of chondritic achondrites.

The unclassified achondrite on the far left is Calivo, also discarded by Urey and Craig (1953). However they discarded it not only because of its low magnesium content but also because of its very high nickel-iron and sulfide content.

The mechanism for producing the two different starting magmas is apparently a reduction of ferrous iron in the silicate phase to metallic iron and the subsequent separation of the two immiscible phases, iron-nickel and silicate.

Figure 6 shows the positions of the mean values of the three carbonaceous chondrite groups

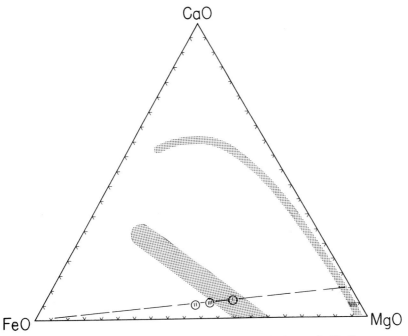

Figure 6. Weight percent CaO, MgO and FeO
diagram showing the mean compositions of the
silicate phase of the three carbonacious chondrite groups given by Wiik (1956), and the
fractionation trends from Figure 5.

given by Wiik (1956) in his paper on the chemical composition of some stony meteorites. Also
shown in the figure are the fractionation trends
derived from Figure 5.

If we consider these carbonaceous chondrites
as the primary starting material and reduce the
FeO in them to iron metal we get a composition
change shown by the dashed line in Figure 6.

This curve lies between the chondritic and a-
chondritic type achondrites and both could be
formed by mineral fractionation of a melt of
the appropriate composition. In order to get

the bustites from a melt on the composition
curve above it there must be some material higher in calcium etc. left over. The achondrites
in the upper part of the diagram possibly represent this residual material.

The mechanism for the evolution of the achondrites outlined above appears more probable than
the complex manipulations required by Cassigy
(1958). No new chemical relationships or mechan-
isms such as silicate phase immiscibility are
required to produce all the known types of achondrites.

Certainly this theory would be strengthened by
a detailed study of the chemical composition of
the mineral phases present in each individual.
Unfortunately, little applicable work has been
done to date. The excellent study of the Moore
County eucrite by Henderson and Davis (1936) and
Hess and Henderson (1949) stands almost alone as
a complete chemical-mineralogical investigation.
Their observations support the possibility of
crystallization differentiation and accumulation.
Other useful studies include those of Foshag
(1938) on the Pasamonte eucrite, Foshag (1940)
on the Shallowater bustite, Lonsdale (1947) on
the Pena Blanca Spring bustite and Beck and Pa-
paz (1951) on the Norton County nortonite.
Only two of these investigations are on achondrites
in the main sequence; the other three are on the
enstatite rich bustite achondrites.

Further investigation of a more detailed nature would certainly help us to determine the
conditions under which the evolution of the a-
chondrites took place. The above theory does
not specify a one body origin or even for that
matter limit the primary bodies to two. It is
certainly not reasonable to assume that if there
were many parent bodies they should all have
different properties. The main sequence distribution may be made up of samples from different
but similar sources.

The information on the composition of the metal
phase of achondrites is nil. It seems likely
that unless the metal-silicate equilibrium was
changed after the initial reduction process that

a knowledge of the composition of the metal
phase would be invaluable in attacking the problem of the primary environment.

It may also be true that some of the achondrites
are not fractionation products of a magma as such
but have been "sweated" out of chondritic material. Of course any relationships within the a-
chondrites must be correlated with the chondrites
and other types of meteorites which are geneti-
cally related to them on a broader scale. It
may well be that while the differences we see in
achondrites are due to differential reduction
and crystallization while those in the chondrites
are due to differential reduction and melting.

REFERENCES

Beck, C. W. and L. LaPaz. 1951. The Nortonite
  Fall and its Minerology Am. Min. 36 45-59.
Buddington, A. F. 1943. Some Petrological Con-
  cepts and the Interior of the Earth Am. Min.
  28 119-140.
Cassidy, W. A. 1958. Achondrite Investigations
  and their Bearing on the Origin of Tektites
  Geochem et Cosmochim Acta 14, 304-315.
Foshog, W. F. 1938. Petrology of the Pasamonte,
  New Mexico, Meteortie. Am. Journal Sci 235
  374-382.
Foshog, W. F. 1940. The Shallowater Meteorite;
  A New Aubrite. Am. Min. 25, 779-786.
Henderson, E. P. and H. T. Davis 1936. Moore
  County, North Carolina Meteorites-A New Eucrite.
  Am. Min. 21 215-229.
Hess, H. H. and E. P. Henderson. 1949. The Moore
  County Meteorite: A Further Study with Comment
  on its Primordial Environment. Am. Min. 34
  494-507.
Leonard, F. C. 1956. A Classificational Catalog
  of the Meteoritic Falls of the World. U. Calif.
  Pub. in Astronomy Z (1) 1-80.
Lonsdale, J. T. 1947. The Pena Blanca Spring Me-
  teorite, Brewster County, Texas Am. Min. 32
  354-364.
Prior, G. T. 1916. On the Genetic Relationship
  and Classification of Meteorites Min. Mag. 18

26-44

Tilley, C. E. 1950.   Some Aspects of Magmatic
  Evolution. Quant. J. Geo. Soc. London 56,44

Urey, H. C. and H. Craig. 1953. The Composition
  of the Stone Meteorites and the Origin of the
  Meteorites. Geochem. et Cosmochem. Acta 4
  36-82.

Wiik, H. G. 1956.   The Chemical Composition of
  some Stony Meteorites, Geochim. et Cosmochim.
  Acta 9 279-289.

Yavnell, A. A. 1956.   Regularities in the Composition of Meteorite Substance and a Classification of Iron Meteorites Geochemistry (2)
  203-219.

JOHN F. LOVERING

Australian National University

The Evolution of the Meteorites—

Evidence for the Co-existence of Chondritic,

Achondritic and Iron Meteorites

in a Typical Parent Meteorite Body

The three currently argued theories concerning the evolution of the meteorites differ primarily on their interpretations of two fundamental points - (i) the sizes of the parent meteorite bodies and (ii) whether the chondrite, achondrite and iron meteorites evolved together in common parent bodies or whether the achondrite and iron meteorites evolved in "primary" parent bodies while the chondrites formed in separate "secondary" bodies.

In Urey's model (Urey, 1959), the achondrites and iron meteorites formed in primary bodies of lunar size while the chondrites were synthesised in secondary bodies of asteroidal size from the products of disintegration of the primary bodies. An important feature of Urey's model of chondrite formation is that the chondrites were compacted in the secondary bodies under varying but generally low temperature conditions. In these circumstances it would not seem possible to expect the co-existence of chondritic material and once-molten metal phase in a single meteorite.

Other works, notably Anders and his co-workers

179

(Fish, Goles and Anders, 1960; Anders and Goles, 1961) and Mason (1960), have proposed that the chondrites, achondrites, and iron meteorites all developed in parent bodies which were of aster-oidal size only. All the known types of meteor-ites have been described as having evolved with-in these small parent bodies - the iron, palla-sites and achondrites from the melted core; the mesosiderites and crystalline chondrites from the deeper regions of the sintered mantle; the more friable chondrites from the intermediate and upper layers; the carbonaceous chondrites from the consolidated surface regions (Anders and Goles, 1961).

The third theory proposes that the meteorites have evolved in a single parent body, or perhaps a small number of similar bodies, of planetary dimensions. The concept of an earth-like parent for meteorites was first advanced by Boisse over a century ago and it is still very attractive to a number of present day workers. Brown and Pat-terson (1948) were responsible for the first modern evaluation of the evidence for a plane-tary parent meteorite body but since then a num-ber of workers have presented evidence which would seem to indicate that the meteorites have evolved in parent bodies of generally lunar di-mensions (e.g., Uhlig, 1954; Lovering, 1957b; Ringwood, 1960; Lovering and Parry, 1961).

It should be pointed out that the asteroidal and planetary parent body models have one very important feature in common - the possible co-existence of chondrite, achondrite, stony-iron and iron meteorites in one or more parent bodies. The only point at issue between the two models is simply the size of the parent bodies. On the other hand the Urey model for meteorite evolu-tion requires that chondrites and liquid metal phase (from which the iron meteorites have crys-tallised) can never have been associated with each other in either the primary or secondary parent bodies. If it can be established that such an association never existed, then it is strong circumstantial evidence in support of Urey's model. However, if such an association

can be established then either his model must be
drastically modified or else the asteroidal or
planetary parent bodies are to be preferred as
the more reasonable models.

It is the purpose of this contribution to review the available evidence bearing on the association of the various types of meteorites in
typical parent bodies. New evidence will be
presented from current textural, compositional
and magnetic studies on meteorites to show that
all the various types of meteorites have formed
in close association with each other in one or
more parent meteorite bodies. It will not be
possible to discuss here the relative merits of
the rival asteroidal and lunar parent body models. The case for asteroidal size parent bodies
has been strongly argued by Anders and Goles
(1961) while the evidence for the operation of
lunar pressures in the central region of a parent body has been recently discussed by Lovering and Parry (1961).

ACHONDRITE - IRON METEORITE ASSOCIATIONS

Pallasites: Olivine achondrite - iron meteorite associations.

A detailed examination of the pallasite stony-
iron meteorites has indicated that these meteorites represent accumulations of olivine crystals
(i.e. an olivine achondrite) intruded by a liquid iron-nickel melt which also contained a
considerable proportion of iron sulphide (Lovering, 1957a). The mean composition of the olivine achondrite portion calculated from selected analyses of olivines from pallasites (table
I) is in good agreement with published and unpublished determinations of the optical properties of the olivines which indicate forsterite
contents of between 86 and 90 mol. per cent.
The nickel, cobalt, gallium and germanium contents of the metal phase in pallasites are remarkably constant and these and other data have
been used elsewhere to show that the metal phase
of pallasites represents samples of the parent
metal melt from which all the various types of

TABLE I.   Selected analyses of olivines from pallasites.

	ADMIRE (This work, W.J. Blake, analyst.)	BRENHAM (Eakins, 1891)	HUCKITTA (Madigan, 1939)	MOLONG (Mingaye, 1916)	MEAN (Recalculated)
SiO_2	40·26	40·70	40·21	40·40	40·29
TiO_2	0·36	–	0·00	–	0·18
Al_2O_3	0·53	–	–	0·17	0·35
FeO	11·33	10·95	12·57	10·35	11·27
MnO	0·25	0·14	–	–	0·20
MgO	47·21	48·02	47·49	47·70	47·50
CaO	0·00	–	0·20	–	0·10
Na_2O	0·00	–	–	–	0·07*
K_2O	0·00	–	–	–	0·01*
P_2O_5	0·03	–	–	–	0·03
Forsterite content (mol. per cent)	87	88	87	89	88

* Data from Edwards (1955).

iron meteorites have differentiated (Lovering, 1957a).

The significance of the pallasites, then, is that their existence demonstrates the close association of the most basic differentiates of the achondritic stony meteorites and the parent melt of the iron meteorites.

Mesosiderites: Basaltic achondrite - olivine achondrite - iron meteorite associations.

Prior (1918) carried out an examination of the mesosiderite group of stony-iron meteorites and concluded that they are actually basaltic achondrites (i.e. pigeonitic-pyroxene anorthitic-plagioclase assemblages, also known as eucrites) which have been intruded by pallasitic magmas. A re-examination of a number of mesosiderites has shown that Prior's conclusions are broadly true in that the mesosiderites are certainly mixtures of basaltic achondrites, olivine achondrite and metal phase portions but the relationships of these various portions are more complex than he suggested. For example, thin-section examination of the Pinnaroo mesosiderite has shown that the margins of the large forsterite-rich olivine crystals (up to 2 cms. in diameter) occurring in the meteorite have been intruded and disrupted by the basaltic achondrite groundmass (figure 1) so that the olivine crystals must have been xenocrysts in the basaltic achondrite magma. The textural relations of the metal phase with the basaltic achondrite groundmass suggests that both components were liquid at the same time and that they solidified in situ (Alderman, 1940). According to Prior (1918) the composition of the metal phase in mesosiderites is the same as that in the pallasites so that the Pinnaroo mesosiderite may have formed from pallasitic material, consisting of olivine crystals in liquid metal phase, which was intruded by a basaltic achondrite magma.

In other cases (e.g., the Dyaul Island mesosiderite) it would seem that the basaltic achondrite magma had crystallised before the intrusion of the metal magma since some pyroxene and

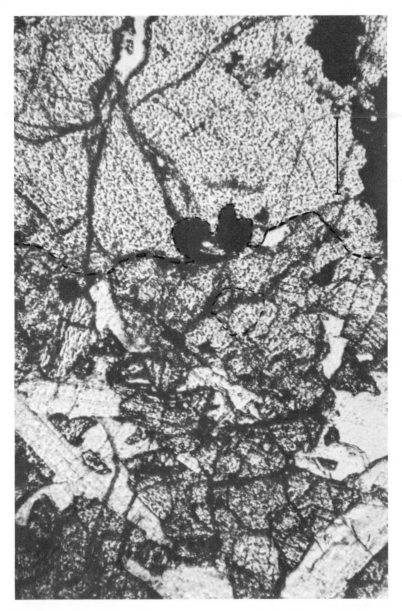

Figure 1:   The Pinnaroo mesosiderite. Large
olivine xenocryst (top) intruded and broken
up by a basaltic achondrite magma (bottom).
Thin section, scale 0.2 mm.

feldspar crystals from the basaltic achondrite
groundmass caught up in the metal phase show
evidence of high temperature metamorphism and
incipient melting.

The Linwood iron meteorite: A pyroxene achondrite - iron meteorite association.

Henderson and Perry (1949) described the Linwood iron meteorite as an irregular coarse octahedrite with many silicate inclusions. Textural-
ly the metallic matrix may be shown to have intruded the silicate inclusions which are mostly
enstatite and olivine crystals with a little
clino-pyroxene and oligoclase feldspar. The silicate assemblage is identical with that of an
enstatite achondrite or bustite so that the Linwood iron meteorite may be interpreted as an enstatite or pyroxene achondrite which has been
intruded by liquid metal phase.

Origin of achondritic, stony-iron and iron meteorites.

It seems reasonable to assume that the observed close association of achondritic and iron meteorite components in certain types of meteorites
points to a common genesis for the achondrites
and iron meteorites in the parent meteorite
bodies.   However, it is not possible to conclude from this evidence alone whether the a-
chondrites and irons evolved in Urey's primary
bodies or in parent bodies of asteroidal or
planetary dimensions along with the chondrites.

However, the observed achondrite-iron meteorite associations do suggest that the various a-
chondrite differentiates (i.e. the olivine ac-
cumulates in pallasites, the enstatite achondrites and the basaltic achondrites) have evolved in close association with metal melts from
which the iron meteorites have formed. A detailed model for the evolution of the achondritic
and iron meteorites will be discussed elsewhere
but it is suggested here that the achondrites
and the iron meteorites have differentiated from
the silicate and metal fractions respectively of
average "normal" chondritic material which has

been completely melted in the parent meteoritic
body.

CHONDRITE - ACHONDRITE ASSOCIATIONS

The Cumberland Falls stony meteorite.
    The classical example of the unequivocal phy-
sical association of chondritic and achondritic
material in a single meteorite is that of the
Cumberland Falls meteorite (Merrill, 1920). In
this unique meteorite angular fragments of a
white, brecciated enstatite achondrite (bustite)
are associated with angular fragments of a black,
highly compacted chondrite along with metal,
troilite and graphite grains (figure 2). Slick-

Figure 2.   The Cumberland Falls stony meteorite.
Enstatite achondrite fragments (white) mixed
with metamorphosed hypersthene-olivine chondrite
fragments (black). Scale 1 cm.

ensided surfaces are common and both the achondritic and chondritic fragments show interpene-
tration textures along their boundaries with
each other on a microscopic scale. These observations indicate that both types of fragments
accumulated together and the physical mixture
was subsequently compressed and compacted. There
is no evidence either from Merrill's work (Merrill, 1920) or the present work to support
Anders and Goles (1961) conclusion that the chondritic fragments are embedded in a groundmass of
the achondritic material.

The white achondrite fragments consist mostly
of large crystals and angular fragments of enstatite which in thin section are often twinned
and show evidence of strain. Clino-pyroxene
grains, some as large as the biggest enstatite
crystals present, are commonly found in association with the enstatite crystals. There are
also occasional oligoclase feldspars which are
apparently interstitial between the pyroxene
crystals. The chemical composition of the achondrite fragments is very similar to that of the
average bustite (table II).

The black chondrite fragments are typically
highly metamorphosed (i.e. heated and compacted)
"normal" chondrites and are not enstatite chondrites as reported by Anders and Goles (1961).
From the point of view of the evolution of the
chondritic meteorites it is very important that
the chondrite fragments be correctly identified
since recent chemical evidence (e.g., Reed,
Kigoshi and Turkevich, 1960) suggests significant differences between the so-called "normal"
chondrites, on one hand, and the carbonaceous
and enstatite chondrites, on the other. However, there is no doubt from analytical data reported by Merrill (1920) as well as from recent
thin-section examination, that at least the major proportion of the chondrite fragments in the
Cumberland Falls meteorite are "normal" metamorphosed chondrites of the hypersthene-olivine
type (table II).

The existence of achondrite-chondrite mixtures
in the Cumberland Falls meteorite has been used

TABLE II.   Composition of the chondrite and a-
chondrite portions of the Cumberland Falls meteorite compared with the average hypersthene-
olivine chondrite and bustite respectively.

| | AVERAGE HYPER-STHENE-OLIVINE CHONDRITE* | CUMBERLAND FALLS METEORITE | | AVERAGE BUSTITE*** |
		Chondritic portion**	Achondritic portion**	
SiO_2	39.57	41.68	55.17	57.44
TiO_2	0.14	-	-	0.06
Al_2O_3	2.70	1.54	0.38	0.96
Cr_2O_3	0.40	0.59	0.06	0.07
FeO	13.33	9.40	2.91	1.72
MnO	0.28	0.09	0.11	0.20
MgO	24.50	27.85	38.73	37.52
CaO	1.75	4.06	1.59	1.13
Na_2O	0.82	tr	0.16	0.60
K_2O	0.16	tr	0.15	0.04
P_2O_5	0.26	tr	tr	0.26
C	0.06	0.45	-	-
Fe	7.76	7.83		
Ni	1.19	0.92		
Co	0.06	0.08		
FeS	6.53	6.74		

* Average of 7 analyses. Data reported by Wiik
(1956) and Mason and Wiik (1960).
** Recalculated from data reported by Merrill
(1920).
*** Recalculated from data reported by Urey and
Craig (1953) and Edwards (1955).

by Urey (1959) as evidence supporting his primary body-secondary body theory. On the other
hand Anders and Goles (1961) have interpreted
Cumberland Falls as evidence contradicting Urey's
model. According to Anders and Goles, Cumberland
Falls

"represents the inclusion of chondrite fragments in an achondrite matrix clearly of
later origin, whereas in Urey's model the
achondrites are made in the primary bodies,
before the synthesis of the chondrites".
However, it has already been shown that there is
no textural evidence to support their contention
that the chondrite fragments in Cumberland Falls
are embedded in an achondrite matrix so that
their criticism of Urey's interpretation is not
valid. All that can be said is that the Cumberland Falls meteorite does show that, at some
time during the evolution of the meteorites, enstatite achondrite and hypersthene-olivine chondrite fragments were mixed and compacted together.
These processes may have taken place in one of
Urey's secondary bodies or in one of the parent
bodies (asteroidal or planetary) in which all
the various types of meteorites formed.

There is, however, one indirect piece of evidence from the Cumberland Falls meteorite which
would seem to support the view that all the meteorites formed together in the parent meteorite
bodies. The chondrite fragments are black, highly compacted chondrites, often with thin metal
veins, which would indicate that they are highly
thermally metamorphosed chondrites. The available evidence suggests that these chondrite fragments were metamorphosed before they were mixed
with the achondrite fragments since the achondrites do not show any effects of this thermal
metamorphism. It may be dangerous to conclude
that the temperature rise associated with the
thermal metamorphism of chondrites was also responsible for forming silicate and metal melts
from which the achondritic and iron meteorites
differentiated, but this would certainly explain
the close association of achondritic and metamorphosed chondritic material in the Cumberland

Falls meteorite. This interpretation has also
been supported by Stacey, Lovering and Parry
(1961) in their explanation of the observed natural magnetic moments in metamorphosed chondrites.
They have concluded that these magnetic moments
are strongly suggestive of the existence of liquid metal cores in the parent chondrite bodies
at the time the chondrites were metamorphosed.
It does not seem possible to reconcile Urey's
model for the evolution of achondrites and iron
meteorites in primary bodies and chondrites in
secondary bodies with these conclusions.

CHONDRITE - ACHONDRITE

IRON METEORITE ASSOCIATION

The Bencubbin stony-iron meteorite.

The Bencubbin stony-iron meteorite was originally described by Simpson and Murray (1932) as
a mesosiderite but a recent re-examination has
shown that it is not a mesosiderite in the generally accepted sense of the term (see discussion
above). A number of sections cut through the
meteorite have shown that it is composed of a
unique association of achondritic and various
chondritic fragments embedded as xenoliths in
an iron meteorite groundmass (Lovering, 1961).
Textural evidence supports the conclusion that
the parent material was an intimate mixture of
pyroxene-olivine achondritic and various chondritic fragments broadly comparable to the association observed in the Cumberland Falls meteorite. At some later stage this physical mixture of stony-meteorite types was intruded by
a metal magma which caught up a number of chondritic and achondritic fragments as xenoliths.
There is ample textural evidence to indicate
that both the achondrite and chondrite fragments
were formed and mixed together before the introduction of the metal phase (figure 3). It does
not seem possible to explain the evolution of
the Bencubbin stony-iron on the basis of Urey's
concept of primary and secondary parent meteorite bodies. The only satisfactory explanation
must assume that chondritic, achondritic and

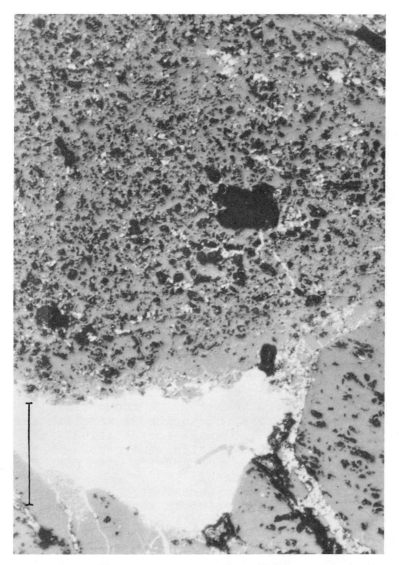

Figure 3.   The Bencubbin stony-iron meteorite.
Junction of white achondrite fragment (bottom
right) with chondrite type 2 fragment (top)
showing intrusion of metal phase along the junction.   Polished section, scale 0.1 mm.

iron meteorites were associated, and presumably
evolved, in common parent meteorite bodies.

A study of the various types of stony-meteorites co-existing as xenoliths in the Bencubbin
stony-iron has also provided new information concerning the evolution of the stony-meteorites
within a common parent meteorite body. For example, at least three types of chondrites have
been recognised as xenoliths. The most abundant
type (chondrite 1) is a black, metamorphosed
hypersthene-olivine chondrite (figure 4) poor in
metal phase (i.e. about 5 per cent) and a member
of the low-iron group of chondrites (Wiik, 1956).
The next most abundant type (chondrite 2) is
very black and compacted (i.e. metamorphosed) in
hand specimen (figure 4). Optical and X-ray
studies show that this chondrite consists of incipient, flattened olivine chondrules embedded
in a dark amorphous-looking matrix containing a-
bundant troilite, about 1 per cent graphite and
less than 2 per cent metal phase. The olivine
is relatively fayalite rich (56 mol. per cent
fayalite) and this fact, coupled with the physical appearance, high carbon and low metal phase
content, indicates that this chondrite is a
highly oxidized type transitional between the
true volatile-rich carbonaceous chondrites and
the normal hypersthene-olivine chondrites.

A third chondrite (chondrite 3) xenolith was
found but it was too small for detailed study.
However, a polished section study shows it to be
a black, metamorphosed chondrite with more than
10 per cent metal phase.

It is of some importance that the three chondrite xenoliths occurring in the Bencubbin
stony-iron are representative of types which
have undergone widely varying amounts of reduction according to Mason's scheme for the evolution of the chondrites (Mason, 1960). The least
reduced type is chondrite 3 with less than 2 per
cent metal phase, while chondrite 1 contains 5
per cent metal and chondrite 2 more than 10 per
cent metal. Representative chondrites from
each of these groups do not always show thermal
metamorphic effects but all three chondrites in

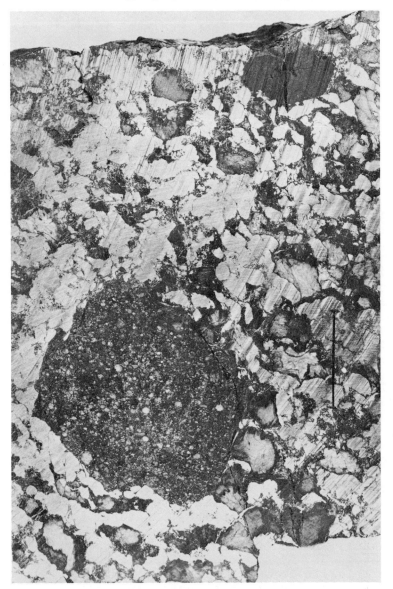

Figure 4.   The Bencubbin stony-iron meteorite.
Chondrite type 1 (bottom left), chondrite type
2 (top right) and white achondrite fragments
intruded by metal phase.   Scale 2 cm.

the Bencubbin stony-iron had been thermally metamorphosed. This would suggest that their metamorphism took place after they went through the
reduction process. If the metamorphism of the
chondrites was contemporaneous with the melting
of the achondrite and iron meteorites, it would
seem that the chondrite reduction process also
pre-dated the evolution of the achondrite and
iron meteorites.

SUMMARY

The observed co-existence of chondritic and
achondritic fragments in an iron meteorite has
demonstrated that all the meteorites must have
evolved together in a single parent body or else
in a number of similar parent bodies. On the
evidence presented here it is not possible to
conclude whether these parent bodies were of asteroidal or lunar dimensions. However, it can
be said that the evidence does not support Urey's
theory that achondritic and iron meteorites were
formed in primary bodies while chondrites accumulated in secondary bodies.
A re-examination of textural and other relations
within the various types of meteorites has suggested the following stages in the evolution of
the parent bodies:
Stage 1: Reduction of primary volatile-rich
carbonaceous chondrite material to form the various types of chondrites (after Mason, 1960).
Stage 2: Metamorphism of the chondritic material with some melting and subsequent differentiation of this melted material to form achondrites and iron meteorites. Natural magnetic
moments of chondrites acquired at this stage
(Stacey, Lovering and Parry, 1961).
Stage 3: Mixing of achondritic and chondritic
material to form Cumberland Falls meteorite. Intrusion of liquid metal phase into achondrite-
chondrite mixture to form Bencubbin stony-iron
meteorite. Intrusion of liquid metal phase into
achondritic material forms pallasites and mesosiderites.
A schematic outline for the evolution of the

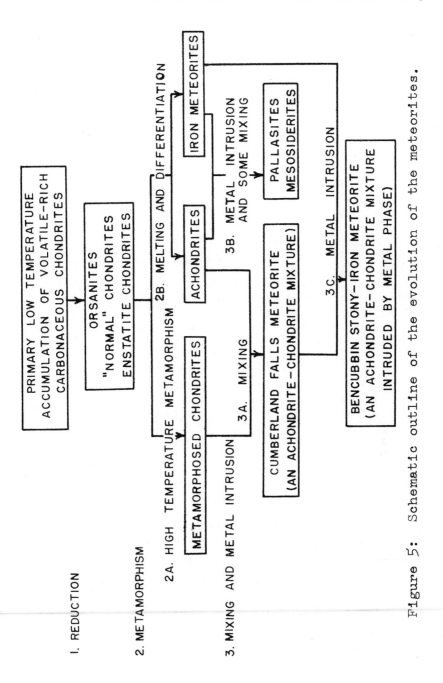

Figure 5: Schematic outline of the evolution of the meteorites.

meteorites based on these conclusions has been given in figure 5. A more detailed discussion is currently in preparation.

ACKNOWLEDGMENTS

The meteorites described in this work were made available by Dr. W.D.L. Ride, Perth Museum; Dr. J.W. Evans and Mr. R.O. Chalmers, The Australian Museum; Professor A.R. Alderman, University of Adelaide. Their ready co-operation is very much appreciated.

REFERENCES

Alderman, A.R. 1940. A siderolite from Pinnaroo, South Australia, Trans. Roy. Soc. South Australia., 64, 109.

Anders, E., and G.C. Goles. 1961. Theories on the origin of meteorites, J. Che. Ed., 38, 58.

Brown, H., and C. Patterson. 1948. The composition of meteoritic matter. III. Phase equilibria, genetic relationships and planet structures, Journ. Geol., 56, 85.

Eakins, L.G. 1891. Seven new meteorites, U.S. Geol. Surv. Bull. No. 78, 91.

Edwards, G. 1955. Sodium and potassium in meteorites, Geochim. et Cosmochim. Acta, 8, 285.

Fish, R.A., G.C. Goles, and E. Anders. 1960. The record in the meteorites. III. On the development of meteorites in asteroidal bodies, Astrophys. J., 132, 243.

Henderson, E.P., and S.H. Perry. 1949. The Linwood (Nebraska) meteorite, Proc. U.S. Nat. Mus., 99, 357.

Lovering, J.F. 1957a. Differentiation in the iron-nickel core of a parent meteorite body, Geochim. et Cosmochim. Acta, 12, 238.

Lovering, J.F. 1957b. Temperature and pressures within a typical parent meteorite body, Geochim. et Cosmochim. Acta, 12, 253.

Lovering, J.F. 1961. The Bencubbin meteorite: New data on the evolution of the meteorites, (in preparation).

Lovering, J.F., and L.G. Parry. 1961. Thermomagnetic analysis of co-existing nickel-iron phases in iron meteorites and the thermal histories of the meteorites, Geochim. et Cosmochim. Acta, (submitted for publication).

Madigan, C.T. 1939. The Huckitta meteorite, Central Australia, Min. Mag., 25, 353.

Mason, B. 1960. The origin of meteorites, J. Geophys. Res., 65, 2965.

Mason, B. and H.B. Wiik. 1960. The Tomhannock Creek, New York chondrite, Min. Mag., 32, 528.

Merrill, G.P. 1920. The Cumberland Falls, Whitley County, Kentucky, meteorite, Proc. U.S. Nat. Mus., 57, 97.

Mingaye, J.C.H. 1916. Notes on the Molong meteorite, Rec. Geol. Surv. N.S.W., 9, 161.

Prior, G.T. 1918. On the mesosiderite-grahamite group of meteorites, Min. Mag., 28, 151.

Reed, G.W., K. Kigoshi, and A. Turkevich. 1960. Determinations of concentrations of heavy elements in meteorites by activation analysis, Geochim. et Cosmochim. Acta, 20, 122.

Ringwood, A.E. 1960. Cohenite as a pressure indicator in iron meteorites, Geochim. et Cosmochim. Acta, 20, 155.

Simpson, E.S., and D.G. Murray. 1932. A new siderolite from Bencubbin, Western Australia, Min. Mag., 23, 33.

Stacey, F.D., J.F. Lovering, and L.G. Parry. 1961. Thermomagnetic properties, natural magnetic moments and magnetic anisotropies of some chondritic meteorites, Journ. Geophys. Res., 66, 1523.

Uhlig, H.H. 1954. Contribution of metallurgy to the origin of meteorites. Part 1. Structure of metallic meteorites, their composition and the effect of pressure, Geochim. et Cosmochim. Acta, 6, 282.

Urey, H.C. 1959. Primary and secondary objects, Journ. Geophys. Res., 64, 1721.

Urey, H.C., and H. Craig. 1953. The composition of the stone meteorites and the origin of the meteorites, Geochim. et Cosmochim. Acta, 4, 36.

Wiik, H.B. 1956. The chemical composition of some stony meteorites, Geochim. et Cosmochim. Acta, 9, 279.

A. E. RINGWOOD

Australian National University

Present Status of

the Chondritic Earth Model

In the past, physical data have provided the principal contribution towards our knowledge of the constitution of the earth's interior. It is now possible to present earth models in which a wide variety of physical properties are reasonably well specified from surface to centre. A requirement for further progress is the correlation of these physical properties with specific chemical compositions, so that a satisfactory chemical earth model can be prepared. Since the problem is beyond the realms of direct observation, and since it is usually possible to find a wide variety of chemical compositions which will satisfy any given set of physical parameters, plausible geochemical models have lagged behind the geophysical models, and an uncomfortably large number have been proposed.

If it would be possible to establish within reasonable limits the net chemical composition of the earth, an enormous simplification would be achieved. In recent years, data on solar and meteoritic abundances and theories of element synthesis have shown signs of convergence, and there are grounds for hoping that a reasonably consistent geochemical composition may eventually be arrived at.

Previous earth models have depended heavily upon the interpretation of meteorite compositions, and it is likely that this position will be maintained. Many geochemists have proposed

198

that the composition of a particular class of
meteorites - the chondrites, provide the most
satisfactory indication of the net chemical composition of the earth. A variety of considerations have been advanced in support of this proposal, e.g.

(a) During the past fifteen years, astronomers
    and geochemists have widely supported the
    view that the solar system was formed from
    a cold cloud of dust and gas. This cloud
    was presumably chemically homogeneous. Ac-
    cordingly, in view of the extreme difficul-
    ties associated with fractionating non vol-
    atile elements within such a cold dust cloud,
    one might expect that the ratios of non-vol-
    atile* elements would be similar in all
    planets, planetoids and satellites which
    formed from this dust cloud. (Ringwood,
    1959). Thus the abundances of non-volatile
    elements in the asteroids, from which mete-
    orites are believed to be derived, should re-
    semble those in the earth. Since chondrites
    comprise about 90 per cent of all meteorite
    falls, the composition of chondrites should
    provide the best indication of average me-
    teorite and asteroidal compositions, and, by
    inference, of the terrestrial composition.

(b) Most workers who have studied the chemistry,
    mineralogy and structures of meteorites also
    agree that chondrites should be representa-
    tive of the average meteorite composition,
    e.g. Urey and Craig (1953); Suess and Urey
    (1956); Ringwood (1959, 1961); Mason (1960,
    a); Fish et al, (1960); and Anders and Goles
    (in press). In addition, Ringwood, Mason,

---

*The term "non-volatile" refers to elements
which were not volatile under the particular
chemical and physical conditions which occurred
during planet formation. According to previous
discussions by the author (1959, 1960) this applies to elements which do not readily volatilize when chondritic material is subjected to
strongly reducing conditions at temperatures up
to 1600°C.

and (apparently) Anders and co-workers, believe that chondrites are of primary origin,
and that other classes of meteorites - a-
chondrites, stony irons and irons - have
formed by the melting and differentiation of
parental chondritic material. Apart from
certain volatile components, chondrites are
remarkably uniform in chemical composition
(Prior, 1913) and appear never to have been
subjected to processes of fractional crystallization (Pinson, 1954).

(c) The abundances of most non-volatile elements
in chondrites are similar to those in the
sun*. (Goldberg, Muller and Aller, 1960).

(d) Chondritic abundances of elements have con-
stituted an important source of data (Suess
and Urey, 1956) upon which theories of element synthesis were developed and tested.
Recent developments (Burbidge et al, 1957:
Cameron, 1959) have succeeded in placing
these theories on a firmer and more independent foundation, so that many of the abundance trends in chondrites can be satisfactorily rationalized in terms of models of
element synthesis which are finding wide
acceptance among astronomers. In a recent
case where serious disagreement occurred between theory and chondritic abundance, subsequent investigation proved that certain

---

*Fe and Cu (but not Ni) may form an important
exception to this generalization. Goldberg et
al (1960) find that the abundance of Fe relative
to other common elements (e.g. Si) is lower by a
factor of 8 in the sun, than in chondrites. However the results of different investigators are
in conflict. For example, Claas (1951) obtained
a similar solar iron abundance to that in chondrites. Apparently the discrepancy is caused by
the selection of different sets of lines for investigations, and by the choice of different
solar atmosphere models. Aller (personal communication) does not consider that the question of
the solar iron abundance has been finally settl-
ed.

rare classes of chondrites indeed possessed
the predicted abundances (Reed et al, 1960).
Thus the increasing degree of internal con-
sistency between fundamental theory and chondritic abundances provides support for the
view that chondritic abundances are in a
sense, primitive and fundamental.

(e) Chondrites consist of a mixture of silicate
and metal phases. If a large body of chondritic material was melted, the metal would
separate out into a core, suggesting an a-
nalogy with the earth. Moreover, petrolo-
gists have noted that the silicate phase of
chondrites forms a useful petrological model
for the earth's mantle (Bowen, 1928). A
partly reduced chondritic mantle can satisfy
the available geophysical data on the mantle
(Birch 1952, Ringwood 1958), when allowance
is made for probably high pressure phase
changes.

In its simplest form, the chondritic earth
model encounters an immediate difficulty. The
average chondrite contains only 13 per cent of
its mass. Furthermore the $\frac{FeO}{MgO}$ ratio of the
average chondrite appears to be much higher than
in the earth's mantle (Ringwood, 1959). When
the $\frac{FeO}{MgO}$ ratios of the earth and chondrites are
brought into agreement by reducing excess FeO to
Fe metal, an excess of SiO_2 appears in the silicate phase of the chondrites. A possible explanation of these difficulties was provided by
Ringwood (1958, 1959, in press), MacDonald and
Knoff (1958) and MacDonald (1959), who suggested
that the relative abundances of metals remained
similar in both chondrites and the earth, whilst
the total oxygen contents differed. Thus, a satisfactory geochemical model could be provided by
reducing the excess FeO and SiO_2 in the silicate
phase of chondrites, and transferring the re-
sultant elemental Fe and Si to the metal phase.
In this way, a correct core-to-mantle ratio can
be obtained, together with a plausible mantle
composition. A variety of independent evidence
supporting this hypothesis was presented by the

above authors. A chondritic model therefore appeared satisfactory for <u>major elements</u>. An attractive feature of this hypothesis was that the varying densities of terrestrial planets, asteroids and satellites could be explained on the same assumptions, without requiring chemical differentiation of major non-volatile elements.

More recently, one of the basic observational "facts" upon which the chondritic earth model was based has been destroyed.

Chondrites are not uniform in chemical composition. Reed et al (1960) have found variations by factors of 10 to 1000 in the amounts of Pb, Tl, Bi and Hg occurring in enstatite, normal, and carbonaceous chondrites. Substantial variations in Se and Te have also been found by Du Fresne (1960). In addition, small but significant variations in K, Na (Edwards and Urey, 1955); Ca (Wiik, 1956); Ba (Reed et al, 1960); Fe and Ni (Urey and Craig, 1953); and xenon isotopes (Reynolds, 1960 a,b) are found among chondrites.

When these variations are considered, one might be surprised that the hypothesis of uniform chondritic composition was ever advanced. However, nearly all the variations are restricted to enstatite and carbonaceous chondrites, which comprise only 6 per cent of known chondrites, and are frequently inaccessible to research workers. Accordingly most work has been carried out on the common "ordinary chondrites" which are very uniform. Despite the variations mentioned, it should not be forgotten that most of the major elements, and very many minor ones, are still comparatively uniform in all classes of chondrites.

In view of these differences the concept of a "primitive" chondritic composition becomes uncertain. Which group is to be chosen? A simple average would hardly be relevant.

It seems that we have reached the stage when the justification for a chondritic earth model depends upon further understanding of the genesis of chondrites and the fractionation processes which have produced their varying compositions.

The Basis of a Chondritic Earth Model

Numerous theories of meteorite genesis have been proposed in recent years - e.g. Urey, (1956, 1957, 1958); Ringwood (1959, 1961); Fish, Goles and Anders (1960); Mason (1960 a,b) and Anders and Goles (in press). Whilst these theories differ in many major respects, it is encouraging to note that partial agreement has been reached in several important fields. Thus, Ringwood, Mason, and perhaps Anders and Goles, would agree that chondrites are the most primitive group of meteorites, and that other classes of meteorites have been formed by the melting and differentiation of parental chondritic material. Furthermore, they would probably agree with Urey's original suggestion* that a particular class of chondrites - the carbonaceous chondrites represent the closest approach which we possess to the primordial dust from which the solar system was formed. Thus, carbonaceous chondrites are regarded as parental to other types of chondrites. As Urey (1953) has pointed out, carbonaceous chondrites are probably much more abundant components of asteroidal matter than their terrestrial occurrence (approximately 4 per cent of observed falls) would suggest. They are extremely fragile, and posses much smaller chances of surviving asteroidal collisions and atmospheric entry than other tougher and more coherent chondrites.

Some considerations leading towards the view that carbonaceous chondrites may be of primitive origin are as follows.
(i)   Carbonaceous chondrites often contain considerable amounts of primary volatile components - up to 20 per cent of water, 7 per cent of sulphur, 5 per cent of carbon and hydro-carbons, together with small amounts of chlorine, ammonia, and obscure organic compounds. They have also been found to contain primordial rare gases in

---

*Urey has since abandoned this suggestion (Edwards & Urey, 1955) for reasons which appear inadequate to the author. This point is further discussed at a later stage.

in amounts much larger than are found in other
types of chondrites. (Reynolds 1960 a,b; Stauffer (in press). The most volatile rich varieties (e.g. Orgueil) contain few recognisable
minerals, and many of the components appear to
exist in an unstable state of combination. Urey
(1953) has pointed out that this assemblage re-
sembes the condensate which would be expected
from a cold gas-dust cloud of solar composition.
(ii)   Carbonaceous chondrites have formed at
low temperatures and some have never been subsequently heated above 350°C, (Reed et al 1960) or
200°C (Du Fresne and Anders, in press). In
sharp contrast to carbonaceous chondrites, all
other meteorites have undergone a complicated
thermal evolution, which involves subjection to
temperatures of 900°C or more (Ringwood, 1961).
(iii)   Carbonaceous chondrites contain amounts
of Pb, Bi, Tl and Hg (Reed et al, 1960) which
are consistent with modern theories of nucleo-
genesis. These elements are severely depleted
in ordinary chondrites.
(iv)   In contrast to all other chondrites, the
iron and nickel in most carbonaceous chondrites
is completely oxidized. Latimer (1950) and Urey
(1952) have shown that the iron in the accre-
tions from a low temperature (0°C) gas-dust
cloud of solar composition would be completely
oxidized. At temperatures appreciably above 0°C,
iron would be partially or completely reduced to
metal. Accordingly other types of ordinary chondrites which contain metal could not form directly from a cold dust cloud.
(v)   A complete mineralogical and chemical transition is observed between carbonaceous and ordinary chondrites. Ringwood (1961) has presented evidence indicating that ordinary chondrites
are formed when parental carbonaceous chondrite
material is subjected to an appropriate high
temperature processing. Mason (1960 a,b) has
also pointed out that carbonaceous chondrites
appear to be parental to other types of chondrites.
    Carbonaceous chondrites may be characterised
as a group by the presence of appreciable quan-

tities of carbon and hydrocarbons, and by the high state of oxidation of their iron. However, within the group, considerable compositional and structural differences occur. It appears in general, that carbonaceous chondrites may be best regarded as samples of original accreted material which have been subjected to varying degrees of volatile loss and compaction have occurred.

Wiik (1956) has analysed a number of carbonaceous chondrites and has recognised three subgroups. These appear to be mutually transitional. The most primitive is the Orgueil group, which contains around 20 per cent of water, 6 per cent of sulphur, and 3 to 5 per cent of carbon. These grade into the Cold Bokkeveldt group, containing about 10 per cent of water, 3 per cent of sulphur, and less carbon. The Cold Bokkeveldt group grade in turn into the Ornansites, which are more compact and metamorphosed than the others, and are transitional into the ordinary chondrites. These contain normal chondritic amounts of sulphur, usually less than one per cent of water, and around half a per cent of carbon. The metamorphism has been sufficiently strong to cause some carbon to react with oxidised iron and nickel, so that up to 5 per cent of metal is found.

Edwards and Urey (1955) have found that sodium and potassium display a rather wide variation, ranging from normal chondritic values (Orgueil) down to values only a fifth as large (Murray). The average alkali metal content of carbonaceous chondrites is about 30 per cent smaller than that of ordinary chondrites. This observation led Urey to discard his original suggestion that carbonaceous chondrites are of primitive origin.

We have noted already that they have been subjected to varying degrees of a very low grade of metamorphism, resulting in differential loss of volatiles, particularly water. Some of the components of carbonaceous chondrites are water soluble, and they probably include sodium and potassium. During the metamorphism which resulted in loss of water, some migration and loss of

water soluble elements may have occurred, and
this may account for the variations in sodium
and potassium observed by Edwards and Urey. Of
the greatest significance in this respect, is
the fact that the most primitive carbonaceous
chondrites - Orgueil and Ivuna, contain normal
chondritic abundances of sodium and potassium.

From the previous discussion, it is concluded
that carbonaceous chondrites of the Orgueil type
probably represent the nearest approach which
we possess to the composition of the original accreted dust from which the solar system was formed. Accordingly we may accept the abundances of
non volatile elements in this type as being
close to the primordial composition. (Table 1).

Table 1

Atomic percentages of major non volatile
elements in the most primitive class of
carbonaceous chondrites. The values tabu-
lated represent an average of the analyses
of Orgueil and Ivuna by Wiik (1956).

Element	Atomic Percentage
Mg	32.30
Si	30.78
Fe	27.38
Al	2.62
Ca	2.26
Na	1.96
Ni	1.40
P	0.40
Cr	0.38
Mn	0.24
K	0.12
Ti	0.09
Co	0.07
	100.00

Ringwood (1961) has made a detailed study of
the chemical evolution of chondrites and their
oxidation-reduction relationships. It was concluded that ordinary and enstatite chondrites
were formed when primitive material of carbonaceous chondrite composition was subjected to

high temperature ($\sim 1000^{o}C$) under such conditions that melting occurred, and carbon reacted with oxidized iron to produce a metal phase. Subsequently, rapid loss of volatiles (principally CO_2 and H_2O) occurred during volcanic, ignimbritic types of eruptions, resulting in formation of the characteristic chondritic textures.

During this phase of volatile loss, other elements which are volatile around $1000^{o}C$ under reducing conditions would be lost. In the paper cited, the major compositional differences between chondrite groups were attributed to differential volatilization of these elements during the high temperature reduction stage. Formation of the earth by accretion from parental carbonaceous chondrite material has been discussed by the author (1960). Owing to the major role of gravitational energy, the subsequent thermal evolution of the earth differed radically from that of ordinary and enstatite chondrites. Accordingly it would not be justified to take compositions of these chondrite groups as the basis for an earth model.

The previous discussions lead to a reconsideration of the chondritic earth model. Instead of postulating that the present composition of the earth resembles that of any particular group of chondrites, we assume that the chemical composition of the original dust from which earth, meteorites and other planets formed is closely approximated by carbonaceous chondrites of the Orgueil type.

During the formation of planets and planetoids this material has been subjected to high temperature autoreduction. The chemical and physical conditions under which this autoreduction has operated have varied widely for different planets and planetoids. During the reduction processes, elements which were volatile under the particular reduction conditions present became lost in varying degrees, so that final equality in composition between the various planets and planetoids would not be expected.

Chondrites have been subjected to a variety of

reduction conditions, resulting in wide variation in abundances of volatile elements such as
H_2O, S, and C, and also in metals which are readily volatile under high temperature reducing conditions, such as Pb, Hg, Tl, and probably many
related elements. At the same time, remarkably
little fractionation has occurred between major
elements[*] and oxyphile trace elements such as U
(Ahrens, Edge and Taylor, 1960). It appears
then, that fractionation is to be expected mainly among non metals and B sub-group elements.

Consideration of the reduction conditions
which accompanied the formation of the earth implies that the effective mean reduction temperature probably did not exceed 1600°C. (Ringwood,
1959, 1960). This temperature limit is indicated by the amount of silicon which is assumed to
be in the core, together with observations of
crustal and upper mantle abundances of many elements which would be reduced and volatilized
above 1600°C. Reduction on the earth nevertheless proceeded at a much higher average temperature than in chondrites, and it is possible that
more elements may have been fractionated and volatilized. In particular, it is possible that
some alkali metals, which are readily volatile
under reducing conditions around 1600°C (Edwards
and Urey, 1955) may have become depleted.

The preceding discussions lead to the following hypothesis, which would provide severe limi-

---

[*] A slight fractionation of iron and nickel has
occurred between Urey and Craig's (1953) "high"
and "low" groups of chondrites. Ringwood (1961)
has attributed this to sinking of nickel-iron
crystals in chondritic magma, prior to the volcanic and volatile-loss stage. From Wiik's analyses, it is noticeable that ordinary chondrites
are somewhat poorer in calcium than carbonaceous
chondrites, whilst enstatite chondrites are more
strongly depleted in this element. It appears
that some Ca and perhaps Ba (Reed et al, 1960)
may accompany the volatiles which are lost, perhaps owing to solubility in supercritical H_2O -
CO_2 fluids.

tations on any chemical earth model.

The abundances of most A sub-group and transition metals are similar in the earth and in the Orgueil class of carbonaceous chondrites. The relative abundances of many non metals, and some volatile alkali and B sub-group metals may, however, differ significantly.

By studying cases in which the abundances of volatile elements in ordinary chondrites, enstatite chondrites and in the earth differ among themselves, and from those in Orgueil, some valuable clues to the chemical and physical reduction conditions which operated during the formation of the solar system may be obtained.

Comparative abundances of some trace elements in the earth and in meteorites

In the light of the previous discussion we will now consider an important paper by Gast (1960), which deals with the abundances of some trace elements on the earth, in relation to chondritic abundances. He arrives at the following conclusions.

(a) A consideration of strontium isotope ratios implies that the $\frac{Rb}{Sr}$ ratio in the upper mantle is substantially smaller (probably by a factor of three) than in chondrites.

(b) The abundances of alkali metals compared to strontium, barium and uranium are lower in the upper mantle than in chondrites.

(c) The $\frac{Rb}{K}$ ratio in the upper mantle appears to be lower than in chondrites.

(d) The amount of thallium probably present in the earth's crust exceeds by a factor of seven, the total amount of thallium in a (normal) chondritic earth.

Gast points out that the mantle has been subjected to an extreme chemical differentiation with respect to certain trace elements. However the relative fractionations of trace elements referred to in his conclusions are directly contrary to expectations based upon their known petrological behaviour and crystal chemical principles. He suggests two alternative explanations

for his conclusions.
(i)   The chemical composition of the earth dif-
      fers from that of chondrites. The differ-
      ence may be caused by the selective reten-
      tion of volatile and non volatile elements.
      In particular, the alkali metals appear to
      have been volatile during the formation of
      the earth, and have been depleted relative-
      ly to chondrites.
(ii) The earth has the same composition as (nor-
      mal) chondrites. However, potassium, rubid-
      ium and caesium have been preferentially re-
      tained in the deep interior of the earth
      compared to uranium, barium and strontium,
      during the major differentiation which oc-
      curred 4.5 aeons ago. Gast quotes G.D.F.
      MacDonald as suggesting that the implied
      anomalous geochemical behaviour of alkali
      metals is due to a hypothetical high pres-
      sure effect which has completely changed
      their normal chemical properties.
   In the author's opinion, the second explanation is not convincing. During crystallization
differentiation processes in the earth's crust,
the following trends towards concentration in
residual magmas are observed.

$$Rb > Sr$$
$$K > Ba$$
$$Rb > K$$
$$K \equiv U$$

The second explanation therefore implies a complete reversal of the usual geochemical relationships.
   In support of this hypothesis, Gast mentions
that reversals occur in the order of the melting
temperatures of alkali halides under high pressure. However these are hardly relevant to differentiation phenomena in the mantle, where the
fractionation of trace elements depends primarily
upon their ability to enter the lattices of close
packed ferromagnesian silicates in which the
principal cations are relatively small.
   The possibility of electronic rearrangements
in the alkali metal analogous to that which occurs in metallic caesium (but not Cs^+!), (Bridg-

man, 1952), should not be ignored. It would be surprising, however, if these resulted in a systematic reversal of all the low pressure relationships mentioned above. A reversal between K^+ and Rb^+ might be explicable, since differing compressibilities, or electronic transitions, could cause a reversal in their relative radii. However the fractionation between Rb^+ - Sr^{++} and between K^+ - Ba^{++} is primarily dependent upon a charge difference. It is more than difficult to formulate plausible high pressure electronic configurations which would reverse the ionic charges, and produce ions capable of giving rise to the observed geochemical distributions. Before this explanation can be taken seriously, some specific proposals for electronic configurations with the required properties should be advanced.

It should be noted that the "changed electronic configuration" explanation fails to account for the high thallium content of the earth's crust. It is also unable to explain the abundance pattern of alkali metals in calcium rich achondrites (see below). There is abundant evidence that meteorites - particularly the tridymite bearing achondrites - have not formed under the extreme pressure conditions required by the hypothesis. Finally, in view of the differing thermal histories of the earth and chondrites, and the discussion of the consequences of these differences in a previous section, it might appear unnecessary to assume that the alkali metal abundances in the earth are similar to those in chondrites.

Gast's first explanation - that K, Rb and Cs were lost in varying amounts by volatilization from the earth during its formation - appears more attractive to the present author. These elements are well known to volatilize from silicate melts under high temperature reducing conditions (Edwards and Urey, 1955). If much of the earth had been subjected to intense high temperature reducing conditions during its formation, differential loss of alkali metals might be expected. Ringwood (1960) has shown that these conditions probably occurred during the accretion of the earth from parental carbonaceous chondrite material.

Gast showed that calcium rich achondrites possess a similar $\frac{Rb}{Sr}$ ratio to that in the upper mantle, and are relatively deficient in Cs and Rb compared to K. Urey (1956, 1957, 1958) had previously attributed the deficiencies of alkali metals in these achondrites to volatilization. It might be expected that volatility of an element will increase as its ionic potential decreases. Thus, K is more volatile in industrial glasses than Na. Accordingly Rb should be more volatile than K. This is consistent with Gast's conclusions on abundances in achondrites and in the upper mantle.

Gast's work is of crucial importance for the thermal history of the earth, since it implies that the earth has probably lost about 2/3 of its potassium relative to ordinary chondrites. Birch (1958) has shown that the rate of total heat loss at the earth's surface divided by its mass is approximately equal to the rate of heat production per unit mass in ordinary chondrites. The uncertainties in terrestrial heat flow measurements and chondrite radioactivities are such that it is not certain whether the earth is slightly cooling, slightly heating, or is in thermal equilibrium. Three-fifths of the heat generated in chondrites is derived from K^{40} decay. If the earth has lost 2/3 of its potassium relative to chondrites, there can be no doubt that it is now cooling.

Reed et al (1960) have shown that carbonaceous and enstatite chondrites possess more than 100 times as much thallium as ordinary chondrites. Apparently, thallium is readily volatilized from carbonaceous chondrites under conditions of moderate heating and reduction, as have occurred in the case of ordinary chondrites. However under the more intense heating and reduction which were responsible for enstatite chondrites (Ringwood 1961) thallium* was not lost - perhaps ow-

---

* Reed et al have shown that lead and bismuth behave similarly to thallium.

ing to the formation under these conditions of a
compound of low volatility. Thus, the high thallium abundance in the crust is not inconsistent
with the formation of the earth from carbonaceous
chondrite material.

Carbonaceous chondrites frequently possess
somewhat higher calcium, and lower alkali metal
contents than ordinary chondrites. It would be
interesting to determine the strontium isotope
ratios in some of these. Perhaps they might be
closer to the terrestrial ratio than ordinary
chondrites. If so, a more direct relationship
between carbonaceous chondrites and the earth
might be indicated.

Acknowledgments

The author is indebted to Dr. S. R. Taylor for
his comments on the manuscript.

REFERENCES

Ahrens, L.H., R.A.Edge, & S.R.Taylor,(1960). The
uniformity of trace elements in chondrites.
Geochim. et Cosmochim. Acta, 20, 260-272.

Anders, G. and G.G.Goles, Theories on the origin
of meteorites. J. Chem. Ed. In press.

Birch, F. (1952). Elasticity and constitution of
the earth's interior. J. Geophys. Res., 57,
227-286.

Birch, F. (1958). Differentiation of the mantle.
Bull. Geol. Soc. Am., 69, 483-485.

Bowen, N.L. (1928). The Evolution of the Igneous
Rocks, Princeton. Princeton University Press.

Bridgman, P.W. (1952). The Physics of High Pressure. p. 182. Bell and Sons Ltd., London.

Burbidge, E.M., G.R.Burbidge, W.A.Fowler, & F.
Hoyle (1957). Synthesis of the elements in
stars. Rev. Mod. Phys., 29, 547-650.

Cameron, A.G.W. (1959). The origin of the ele-
ments. Physics and Chemistry of the Earth,
Vol. 3, 199-223. Ed. Ahrens et al. Pergamon
Press, London.

Claas, W.J. (1951). The composition of the solar
atmosphere. Recherches Astron. Observ. Utrecht,

XII, Part 1, 1-52.

Du Fresne, A. (1960). Selenium and Tellurium in
Meteorites. Geochim. et Cosmochim. Acta, 20,
141-148.

Du Fresne, E.R. & E.Anders, A thermometer mineral in the Mighei carbonaceous chondrite. Geochim. et Cosmochim. Acta. (In press).

Edwards, G. & H.C.Urey, (1955). Determination
of the alkali metals in meteorites by a distil-
lation process. Geochim. et Cosmochim. Acta.
7, 154-168.

Fish, R.A., G.G.Goles, & E.Anders (1960). The
record in the Meteorites III. On the development of meteorites in asteroidal bodies. Astrop. J., 132, 243-258.

Gast, P.W. (1960). Limitations on the composition of the upper mantle. J. Geophys. Res.,
65, 1287-1297.

Goldberg, L., E.A.Müller, & L.H.Aller (1960).
The abundances of the elements in the solar
atmosphere. Astrop. J. Suppl. 45, Vol. 5,
1-138.

Latimer, W.M. (1950). Astrochemical problems in
the formation of the earth. Science 112, 101-
104.

Mason, B. (1960a). Origin of chondrules and
chondritic meteorites. Nature, 186, 230-231.

Mason, B. (1960b). The origin of meteorites. J.
Geophys. Res., 65, 2965-2970.

MacDonald, G.J.F. & Knopoff (1958). The chemical
composition of the outer core. Geophys. J., 1,
284-297.

MacDonald, G.J.F. (1959). Chondrites and the
chemical composition of the earth. Researches
in Geochemistry ed. Abelson. 476-494. Wiley &
Sons, New York.

Pinson, W.H. (1954). The chemical composition of
meteorites and the shattered planet hypothesis.
Ann. Prog. Rept. M.I.T. Dept. of Geol. & Geophys. D.I.C. PRoject 7033, Part IIIe.

Prior, G.T. (1913). On the remarkable similarity
in chemical and mineral composition of chondritic stones. Min. Mag. 17, 33-38.

Reed, G.W., K. Kigoshi & A. Turkevich (1960).
Determinations of concentrations of heavy

elements in meteorites by activation analysis. Geochim. et Cosmochim. Acta, 20, 122-140.

Reynolds, J.H. (1960 a). Isotopic composition of primordial xenon. Phys. Rev. Letters 4, 351.

Reynolds, J.H. (1960 b). I-Xe dating of meteorites. (Manuscript).

Ringwood, A.E. (1958). Constitution of the mantle, Part III. Geochim. et Cosmochim. Acta, 15, 195-212.

Ringwood, A.E. (1959). On the chemical evolution and densities of the planets. Geochim. et Cosmochim. Acta, 15, 257-283.

Ringwood, A.E. (1960). Some aspects of the thermal evolution of the earth. Geochim. et Cosmochim. Acta, 20, 241-259.

Ringwood, A.E. (1961). Chemical and genetic relationships among meteorites. Geochim et Cosmochim. Acta. (In press).

Ringwood, A.E. (In press). Silicon in the metal phase of enstatite chondrites and some geochemical implications. Geochim. et Cosmochim. Acta.

Stauffer, H. (In press). Primordial argon and neon in carbonaceous chondrites and ureilites. Geochim. et Cosmochim. Acta.

Suess, H.E. & H.C.Urey (1956). Abundances of the elements. Rev. Mod. Phys. 28, 53-74.

Urey, H.C. (1952). The Planets. Yale University Press, New Haven.

Urey, H.C. (1953). Discussion in Nuclear Processes in Geologic Settings, p. 49, N.R.C. Washington, D.C.

Urey, H.C. (1956). Diamonds, meteorites and the origin of the solar system. Astrophys. J., 124, 623-637.

Urey, H.C. (1957). Meteorites and the origin of the solar system. Year Book of the Physical Society, 14-29.

Urey, H.C. (1958). The early history of the solar system as indicated by the meteorites. Proc. Chem. Soc., 67-78.

Urey, H.C. & H. Craig (1953). The composition of the stone meteorites and the origin of the meteorites. Geochim. et Cosmochim. Acta, 4, 36-82.

Wiik, H.B. (1956). The chemical composition of
    some stony meteorites. Geochim. et Cosmochim.
    Acta, 9, 279-289.

H. H. NININGER

Sedona, Arizona

Recovery of Materials

for Meteoritic Research

Obviously meteorites are first in order of importance when considering materials to be investigated in any program of meteoritical research; but there are several other items which cannot be ignored and some of these may prove to be quite as important in the meteoritical program as meteorites themselves. I shall first direct attention to some of these less familiar aspects of the problem.

Meteoritic Dust. Unquestionably the bulk of matter arriving from space reaches the soil in the form of dust or very small particles. All of the grist from the friction mill of the atmosphere including the ash from millions per hour of "shooting stars", ablated particles from surviving meteorites, terminal dust clouds and showers of sand and gravel discharged from stratospheric smash-ups that give us our meteorite showers may be considered under the head of meteoritic dust. The micro-meteorites which, in space, are so small as to filter in unscathed by friction are not considered in this category.

Up to now there has been no adequately planned attack upon the meteoritic dust problem. It therefore offers great possibilities. Several

more or less successful efforts have been made
to measure the magnetic ingredient of this increment; but no satisfactory plan for identification
and measurement of the non-magnetic portion has
ever been put into operation. It is this latter
constituent of the increment that is most important because the overall composition of meteorites
as judged by the study of recovered meteorites
and by spectroscopic analyses of meteor trails
leaves no doubt that stony constituents far out-
weigh the metallic phase.

One method of attack has been sufficiently
tested to seem to justify a serious attempt at
quantitative measurement. The method has the advantage of large scale concentration of the dust
in-fall, thus providing sufficient material for
various types of analyses which should enable
the investigaror to work out satisfactory procedures for identification as well as quantitative
measurement. The plan calls for the selection
of a coral island remote from continents and
other land masses consisting of rock species
that are most likely to be confused with meteoritic minerals. Here a glazed roof of measured
dimensions would be erected and fitted with drain-
age troughs and pipes leading through suitable
traps which could be examined periodically.

In order to detect seasonal variations the roof
should be fitted with a sprinkling system so as
to secure regular runoffs during periods of
drought. Resident investigators would be supplied with laboratory facilities and a staff sufficient so that tolerable tours of service could
alternate with periodic vacation. The experiment
should be carried on through at least three years
in a given location and simultaneously in at
least three different latitudes.

The importance of securing useful quantitative
data on this problem is pointed up by the fact
that various estimates by noted astronomers,
geologists and meteoriticists during the present
century have ranged from 5,000 tons to 18 million
tons per year for this type of meteoritic increment over the whole planet.

Fossil Meteorites: Another type of investiga-

tion should be concerned with the alterations
that accompany the aging of meteorites after
they enter our atmosphere and make contact with
the soil. These weathering processes by which
they eventually lose their identity we call ter-
restrialization. The collection which the
Arizona State University has lately acquired contains specimens whose state of preservation
ranges all the way from that of fresh arrivals
which were picked up within hours after their
landing to those in which the changes wrought by
weathering are so vast that only the most critical examination by experts could verify their
true nature. Several of them were first reject-
ed by leading geologists who, later, when per-
suaded to investigate further recognized indis-
putable evidence, pronounced them meteorites.
I have great confidence that the present generation of scientists with modern equipment, new
techniques and intensified effort, shall be able
to discover reliable clues by which to identify
even the completely altered remains of ancient
meteorites in many of our older geological formations.

Because no authentic meteorite has yet been
found which could be definitely assigned to any
formation older than pleistocene some scientists
have assumed that they are absent from the older
formations. But those who have had most experience in meteoritical field work remain far from
convinced that the failure to find them is sufficient evidence of their absence. Very little
of any old formation is exposed to view except
by the gradual process of erosion which allows
the forces of weathering to render any meteorites
buried therein very difficult to recognize. In
addition to this deterrent it must be admitted
that there has been little or no effort to alert
geologists to be on the lookout for meteorites
of ancient vintage.

Paleontologists are obviously in the best position to come into contact with fossil meteorites
and a single illustration will suffice to demonstrate that the profession has not exhausted the
possibilities along this line.

Some years ago I met one of the world's great
fossil hunters who had spent more than 20 years
as a field man and whose finds had found their
way into most of the world's great museums.
When asked if he had ever found a meteorite the
answer was negative. I spent some time showing
him various samples and in less than 2 years he
found a 130-lb stony meteorite, representing a
previously unknown fall. Others were recovered
by him later. These were not fossil meteorites.
So far as I know there is as yet no very good
criterion by which to recognize fossil meteorites; but with modern technology this need could
doubtless be met.

Impact Scars: In this state of Arizona, within whose borders lies the finest example of meteorite crater known on earth, certainly we cannot be satisfied with the mere study of meteorites themselves. Naturally, the true scientist
is impelled to inquire into the nature of forces
and effects attendant on the instantaneous dis-
placement of a few hundred million tons of rock.
When he considers that twice within a half century, crater-forming meteorites have punctured
the land surface of the earth; that within the
same period mountain-sized asteroids have en-
croached upon the orbital precincts of our planet no less than five times; one of which may
well be described as a lucky near-miss, and then
looks at the pock-marked face of the moon, the
thoughtful scientist is forced to admit that meteorite impacts constitute a geological problem
of considerable magnitude.

Geologists have recently become concerned with
the problem of meteorite impact as a force to
be considered in solving geological problems.
While this paper is in preparation there comes
to my desk an official announcement that the
U.S.Geological Survey has launched a program of
Space Geology supported by NASA which is described as investigations of materials produced by or
associated with meteorite craters or other impact scars. The Department of Mines and Special
Surveys of Canada has been searching for and
exploring ancient traces of meteorite craters

for several years and the USSR has an exceedingly active committee working along similar lines.

From these illustrations it can be seen that the effects of meteorites are equally as important subjects for research as are meteorites themselves.

In recent years several varieties of small particles have been discovered at the site of the Arizona crater, none of which have been adequately studied. Coesite which is a product of pressures and temperatures unknown in crustal rocks and several other varieties of impactite need careful study and numerous other aspects of this great crater have never been adequately investigated. Here are materials for research near at hand.

Meteorites in the Soil: Recovery of meteorites from witnessed fireballs has been described in another paper. Here we shall consider the important matter of recovering meteorites that have arrived at times unknown but which are still recognizable and therefore useful in many ways in our meteoritical program.

The best source of information with respect to methods of operation and what can be accomplished along this line is the record of the Nininger Laboratory, later known as the American Meteorite Laboratory and American Meteorite Museum which in a period of 35 years brought to light more than 200 falls aggregating about 2,000 individual meteorites that were recovered.

This program consisted of lectures in high schools and the upper grades, press notices, lectures to various clubs and other groups, personal contacts and the distribution of literature, in agricultural communities principally in the Plains States of Kansas, Nebraska, Oklahoma, eastern Colorado, eastern New Mexico and in southeast Wyoming. The lectures and literature emphasized the importance of meteorites in research and presented in simple language criteria by which meteorites could be recognized. It offered to test, free of charge, all samples sent in and an offer to purchase after testing, provided the sample proved to be a meteorite.

Miami, Texas, Meteorite

This meteorite lay in his yard for many years after Mr. Thornton plowed it up, then it was used as a "dead man" in fence building. Hearing of this "possible meteorite" through Judge Mead whom he had alerted some years before, Nininger and son, Bob, inspected the "dead men" in that fence. The 26th. one proved to be a 127-lb meteorite.

It is estimated that the program reached five
to ten per cent of the agricultural population
of the above-designated area directly or indi-
rectly. That estimate is probably high rather
than low.

The effectiveness of the program by way of
actual recoveries was given much careful study
and these studies were checked by repeated re-
turns to areas where finds were made. It is the
writer's firm belief that less than 50% of the
finds made by persons who had been alerted
through the program were ever reported to our
organization or to any other institution. The
mental set of individuals who fail to report
finds after having been informed of their value
is one that still baffles all who have partici-
pated in our program. We emphasize this point
for the reason that any who undertake a field
program are most likely to fall down on this as-
pect of it. For example: here is a man who had
found several stones of a fall that had been
witnessed in his community. He knew that a neigh-
bor had been paid 50 cents an ounce for two
stones and that a request had gone out for more.
This man was so poor that his children were kept
out of school for lack of decent clothes yet he
had not so much as carried the meteorites in from
the field. When asked to accompany me to where
I could examine one of the stones he readily
agreed and did subsequently recover some 40 or
50 dollars worth of the stones he had thrown a-
way.

Had we been able to keep a man constantly in
the field it is almost a certainty that our
harvest of meteorites would have been doubled.

In 1930 I resigned my professorship to devote
full time to meteorites. The great depression
reached the west in 1931. The years that followed were hard years but we kept up our search.
Many extensive and expensive projects ended in
failure so far as visible results were concerned.
During those years institutions and individual
collectors bought specimens, books and literature,
but not enough. A small farm, our home and even
some insurance policies were sold. But there

were always just enough fruits of the search to
give me confidence. Our collection was growing
and in a scientific age I could not cease to believe that man's only tangible source of information concerning the universe outside the earth
would soon come to be properly appreciated.

I will give you one or two of the encouraging
episodes that bolstered confidence. (I dislike
to dwell on failures.) His love of the work and
the small salary I paid him made Alex a very
good and loyal worker. I said to him in 1936,
"I want you to go down to Gladstone, New Mexico,
set up your tent and stay three weeks. Keep
your meteorite samples on display in that country
store and try to contact every farmer in that
community. There should be a meteorite somewhere
thereabouts because none has been found nearer
than about 12 miles and quite a lot of land is
under cultivation."

At the end of two weeks he wrote that he had
found no leads; that he had seen every farmer
around there; he himself had walked fields and
pastures until he was so sore and stiff he could-
n't sleep. Should he stay on another week or go
to the next location? I answered, "Stay on".
Three days later he wrote that a rancher who had
been ignoring his display stopped to look and
then said, "Is that the kind of stuff you buy?"
When told that it was he said, "Hell, I've got
one as big as a coal bucket." Alex bought the
128-lb. stone which had been lying up against
the barn since he plowed it up four years earlier.
Within a week Alex heard of and purchased four
others representing three different falls.

At about the worst of the depression a small
sample arrived from Morland, Kansas. It came
from a telegraph operator whom I had met some
years before in another Kansas town. He was
deeply interested in what I was doing. The sample, he said, came from a farmer near Morland
who said he had plowed out a huge mass of several hundred pounds. Financially at that moment
we were scraping the bottom of the barrel. I
had borrowed to my limit at the bank. I went to
my friend Gillespie who always liked to finance

The Harrisonville, Missouri Find

The rock-free fields of a small farming community led Nininger to spend a half day alerting
the farmers. None had ever thought of meteorites; but about 40 stones turned up as a result
of his visit.

Gladstone, New Mexico, Meteorite

This fine example of stony meteorite was
plowed up and discarded as a nuisance. It was
reported 4 years later when the farmer was a-
lerted by the Nininger Laboratory.

a good looking prospect for half interest in the
proceeds. He gave me a check. I went over and
found that the man had a 660-lb. meteorite which
he planned to drag to a nearby ravine and dump it,
angry because it had broken his new plow. I a-
greed to relieve him of the moving of it and pay
him enough to buy a new plow. He had money left
over for I gave him $330.00.

One hot, windy day I sat down at a roadside
stand and ordered a hamburger sandwich and coffee. I laid a small stony meteorite beside my
water glass. Shortly a cattle truck stopped in
front and the driver who entered sat down beside me. He wiped the sweat and grime from his
face, rubbed the sand from his eyes, wiped his
glasses with a napkin, replaced them and then
reached over and picked up the little meteorite,
examined it briefly and replaced it. I said,
"Do you know what it is?" "Well, it looks like
a rock." "Yes, it's rock but a very special one.
It fell from the sky." "Oh, you mean one of
them meters?" "Yes that is a meteorite."

Again he picked it up, hefted it, leaned over
and said, "You're not kidding?" I assured him
I was not. "Are they worth anything?" I explained that in the usual sense of values they were
not; but that to scientists like myself they were
very important as a source of information about
the universe and that we paid good prices for
them.

He took a swig of coffee, wiped his mustache,
examined the meteorite again and said; "You
know, my brother-in-law over in Nebraska may have
one of those things in his yard. It's a big
thing. He bumped into when plowing several years
ago in a field where there were no other rocks.
He brought it up to the house and it's been lay-
in' around in the yard ever since."

I asked him how far we were from his brother-
in-law's place and he said it was 110 miles.
That seemed too far for a wild goose chase so
after discussing the matter I handed him a leaf-
let on how to recognize meteorites and asked him
to give it to his brother-in-law. A few weeks
later I received a sample of an old, weathered

meteorite but it happened to be one of a rather
rare group. When I went over to see it I found
he had about 450 pounds of it in his yard and we
were able to gather another 150 lb. from the
hilltop where he had plowed it up and from a
fence row where he had thrown a 45 lb. fragment.
The large mass had probably fractured on impact
and further broken up by weathering.

I cite these examples to emphasize the evident
fact that many stones valuable for research are
yet lying around farm houses and in fence rows.

I could tell many equally striking experiences
but there were also months on end during which
we worked just as hard, borrowing and spending
without receiving even a sliver of meteorite in
compensation. Such disappointments will doubtless plague any who attempt to harvest the ce-
lestial fruit that from time to time comes to
rest on our planet.